Magnificent MIDLIFE

TRANSFORM YOUR MIDDLE YEARS, MENOPAUSE AND BEYOND

RACHEL LANKESTER

Disclaimer

The contents of this book are for information only and are intended to assist readers in their midlife years and menopause transition. This book is not intended to be a substitute for taking proper medical advice and should not be relied upon in this way. Always consult a qualified doctor or health practitioner. To the extent permitted by law, the author disclaims all responsibility and liability to any person, arising directing or indirectly from any person taking or not taking action based on the information in this publication.

ISBN 978-1-7398115-0-1

Editing by Ricki Heller

Cover design by Vanessa Mendozzi

Internal layout by Euan Monaghan

First published in 2021 by The Mutton Club Limited

To all women who thought menopause and aging somehow lessened them.
They don't.
Midlife and beyond is your time to shine.

CONTENTS

PART TWO: EMBRACING MENOPAUSE: MANAGING THE TRANSITION WITH EASE

PART THREE: LOOKING FORWARD: CRAFTING THE FUTURE OF YOUR DREAMS

FINDING MY PASSION FOR MIDLIFE

*"The end of my fertility has become the
most fertile time of my life."*
Rachel Lankester

How do you feel about being in midlife? Do you dread the "inevitable downward slope?" The invisibility? Do you wonder if you're on the wrong life track? Are you okay about aging but still feel stuck? Wondering when *your* life is going to kick in? You know there's more to life, but how? HOW do you find that more?! If you've thought about any of these issues, this book is for you.

Many women fear aging and see midlife as the beginning of the end. I was one of those women. There's so much rubbish thrown at us about exactly how we should or shouldn't be and what life is going to look like from now on. Perhaps you feel anxious about even accepting you're in midlife. Why does the word "midlife" cause such anxiety? It's such a simple word: the middle of life. Sadly, we've been taught to think midlife is the end of meaningful life, that it's downhill from here.

If you live in a culture like the UK or US, where we overwhelmingly worship youth, it can be very challenging to think otherwise. That's why I wrote this book, to change all that. To challenge outdated and overwhelmingly sexist narratives about aging, disrupt them, and empower you to write your own story about what midlife (and beyond) will be for you. We're going to change all the ageist silliness because change is long overdue. Join me to say "no" to negative midlife nonsense. While we do that, we're going to make your midlife magnificent!

This book does some serious rebranding of midlife and will do the same for *you*. You may be stuck in the messy middle or managing to push your way forward with grace and gumption, but there's a bigger purpose here too. Transformation doesn't mean midlife women changing on their own. The world needs to see us differently, no matter how we see ourselves. Without a shift in how society sees us, we'll be facing an uphill battle forever.

Why do I want to rebrand midlife? How did I get so passionate about changing it? Life rarely works out as we plan, does it? It can throw quite a few curve balls at us. Early menopause at 41 was one of mine.

It became the catalyst for a whole new life, much better than the one before. Looking back, over a decade later, I wouldn't change what happened. This book and everything that's brought me to writing it wouldn't exist without the experience. Let me tell you where my magnificent midlife journey began, and why I think rebranding midlife is *so important*.

I always wanted a big family, at least four children. I made the mistake of falling for a man who wasn't so keen. It took me seven years of persuading to be *allowed* to try for a baby. (I probably should've got that straight before we got hitched!) When a baby came along instantly, it took us both by surprise. No fertility problems then. When my son arrived, I knew immediately I wanted more. Sadly, his father was having none of it.

There were many reasons why my first marriage broke down, and my desire for more children was definitely one of them. After we split, I tried to find a man to make babies with me. I was 35, and the clock was ticking. Turns out, I wasn't very good at finding men I could bend to my will!

I finally fell for a man who already had three children and hadn't planned any more. He'd also had a vasectomy. After much reflection, we finally agreed it'd be wonderful to have a child together, and this amazing man agreed to reverse his vasectomy.

We knew it might not work. But he was willing to give it a go. I was 41 by this stage, so before subjecting my beloved to the knife, it seemed wise to have a hormone test, just to check everything was working on my side. I had no reason to think it wouldn't be.

That's why I was in the doctor's office awaiting my results when the doctor turned to me and said, "Your test results show you've gone through menopause." Say what? "Your FSH[1] levels are those of a postmenopausal woman," he repeated in a slightly different way, as if that made the blindest bit of difference. "You would be unable to conceive a child."

Bomb dropped.

I can't really remember what happened next. I've found I tend to block out the details of unhappy events, which is probably a good thing. I left with a prescription for hormone replacement therapy (HRT)—the one made from pregnant mare's urine, Premarin—the standard recommendation in the UK at that time.

I guess he probably asked if I'd stopped having periods. I hadn't even noticed. I'd recently left a stressful executive job to start working freelance and was full steam ahead finding clients. I hadn't been very happy in my job and was feeling liberated and excited. I was also nervous about *choosing* to be without a job for the first time in my life.

Perhaps it wasn't surprising I hadn't noticed my monthly cycle. I'd never been particularly in tune with it, anyway. With hindsight, I came to learn that was probably part of the problem. Just as when you go on holiday and suddenly get sick, stepping off the stressful corporate hamster wheel allowed my body to say, "I can't keep this show on the road anymore." Hello, early menopause!

I remember feeling life had taken a nasty nosedive. Everything was a blur for quite some time. I didn't fill the HRT prescription. I sat on it for another three years. I came away knowing nothing about why this had happened to me, how to take care of myself, nor what it meant for me to be post-menopausal a whole flipping decade early.

Knowing what I know now, I think the information and care given to me was woeful. The grief came instantly, like a tidal wave. Grief for the child I was never going to have. I knew I was optimistic to expect to get pregnant at 41. I wasn't stupid. It had been the last roll of the dice, so to speak. Getting a diagnosis of early menopause was something else completely.

I sank for a time into real despair. No one had died, but my life-long dream to have a second child was gone. In addition, there was the realization that, according to society or the narrative inside my head, I was now a shriveled up old prune. No one had actually told me that; I came to that conclusion by myself. I had succumbed to decades of relentless messaging that midlife was the beginning of the end, that older women were insignificant. In my head, my lack of fertility meant I'd instantly lost my looks, value, and relevance, and I was destined to life relegated to the back. Dismissed.

I'm a natural researcher, and digging around, I found information—or, at least, where to go to get information. It wasn't easy, which is why I later created the resources I couldn't find. I discovered the Daisy Network,[2] a charity set up to provide information and support for women who've gone through early menopause. They were a fantastic resource, and when I discovered their annual conference, I was there like a shot.

That event was a real eye-opener and quickly shifted me out of self-pity. I felt such a fraud. I already had one child. Most of the women there had gone through menopause significantly earlier. They'd never been able to have children at all.

Some had accepted a childless life, some adopted, some conceived using donated eggs. I briefly considered that last option, but we already had three children whose father was my partner and the mother someone other than me! The sadness of many of the women in the room was palpable, and I realized how lucky I was.

The event introduced me to two people who would play an important part in my menopause journey, Dr. Nick Panay and Dr. Marilyn Glenville. I asked for a referral to Dr. Panay a few years later, when I finally went on HRT. He was the top man in the UK specializing in early menopause. He and his team were brilliant.

My treatment from Dr. Glenville was transformational because, for a time, I got my periods back (yes, really!) It became the formative first step on my journey of discovering just how important diet and lifestyle are in creating and maintaining hormonal balance. I learned that we never have to accept the status quo, and we almost always have choices when it comes to our hormones.

Dr. Glenville suggested there was much she could do to help women struggling with early menopause and infertility. She was crystal clear about my prospects. No guarantees, but if I signed up to her advice for three months, there was a chance I could get my hormones back to premenopausal levels. She told me to cut out alcohol, caffeine, dairy products, and added sugar. I was to eat only organic produce. I should also try to use cosmetic products that were as natural and nontoxic as possible. She wanted me to have a small protein snack every three hours to keep my blood sugar levels stable.

Within five weeks, I had a period! Incredible. I couldn't believe it. From a diagnosis of having gone through menopause, I was now once again bleeding. I had another hormone test, and this doctor said he saw no reason why I couldn't conceive. The love of my life went for the reverse vasectomy, but it didn't work. Nine months later, my periods disappeared again, and another hormone test confirmed I was back to my postmenopausal hormone levels. It was all very confusing.

I now know that hormone fluctuations during our 40s are not abnormal, although it was still rather early for it to be happening to me. I just wish the doctors I saw then had known that too. I also now know menopause is a tiny fraction of a doctor's medical education, with diet being only just slightly more. I now believe my initial diagnosis was most probably wrong. I was in perimenopause rather than definitively through menopause. Our hormone levels fluctuate enormously during the perimenopause years – that period of time leading up to menopause. Technically, you are in menopause when you have had no periods for a year if you're over 50, and two years if you're under 50. So, menopause itself is just a moment in time. I certainly hadn't been without a bleed for two years and if I'd had the hormone test on another day, the results could have been completely different.

Turning around the diagnosis and getting my period back taught me the impact of diet, lifestyle, and mindset in midlife. I'd been running on empty for a long time and living a very stressful and unhappy work life. Falling in love again, while a wonderful thing, is also a stress on the body. I have no doubt the years spent in a highly stressful environment contributed to my hormones going haywire at 41, when I stepped off the hamster wheel. My emotional reaction to what happened made the experience much worse. Thankfully, I eventually figured out I was no less of a woman because I'd supposedly gone through menopause.

Stress messes with our adrenal gland function in particular and our hormones in general. Consider women who finally give up trying to conceive after infertility, adopt, and then conceive naturally. How we respond to our environment and the pressure we put ourselves under both impact our hormonal health. It wasn't until the early menopause diagnosis that I started to consider all this in any meaningful way. We'll be looking at the many ways to get better hormonal balance, through perimenopause and beyond, in this book.

My period disappeared again after nine months. Apparently, it wasn't unusual for the body to revert to its original plan, even though it had been possible to kick-start it back to fertility. I wonder, looking back, if it wasn't also because I reverted to my old bad habits food-wise, including alcohol and sugar. We'll never know.

What I hope you'll learn from my story is that:

- Evidence of hormonal changes is often what makes us realize we're in midlife.
- These changes kick-start a period of intense transformation for which we're usually completely unprepared.
- Hormonal changes, and menopause itself, can happen a lot earlier than we expect.
- Our hormones can fluctuate wildly during our perimenopause years.
- What we eat and drink, and how we live, impacts our hormones massively.
- There is much we can do to improve our own hormonal health.

- It pays to stay curious and challenge what you're told, even by a doctor!
- The period of midlife and menopause is *not* the end of meaningful life; rather, it's an exciting new transition if we choose to embrace it as such.

Without having experienced the early menopause diagnosis, my life would be very different. I'm grateful to it for spearheading a completely different and far more fulfilling life, and for teaching me how women can age when we don't accept the nasty narratives we grow up with. As often happens in life, something bad can produce something magnificent. I now view early menopause as a gift. Without it, I wouldn't be the woman I am today. It prompted me to reevaluate everything about getting older as a woman, to question all those negative ageist and sexist narratives and stereotypes, and to challenge the accepted status quo like a banshee! I want you to feel the power of this time of life too.

In this book, you'll find quite a lot about menopause because I want to empower you to know what's coming and how to deal with it (be prepared, not scared), or help you vibrantly transition through it now. If you're already through menopause, I want to make sure you know how to balance your hormones long-term. Once we've got menopause sorted, we'll move on to the other juicy stuff, the truly magnificent side of midlife and beyond. My aim is to open up possibilities and options for you, so you don't necessarily have to accept the life you've ended up with.

A NEW GUIDE TO THE MIDDLE YEARS, MENOPAUSE, AND BEYOND...

But how do you cope if you're stuck in a midlife funk, unsure of yourself, grappling with menopause and an empty nest, maybe caring for older parents, bored and overwhelmed all at the same time, and generally feel you're constantly pushing water uphill? Stick with me, and I'll show you.

This is your midlife guide to getting the bad stuff sorted and bringing on the *great* stuff. Because quite apart from *you* needing to thrive, not just survive, the world needs us women in top form, don't you think? The world's a mess and crying out for more female energy and power. Just look at which countries dealt better with COVID-19—often led by women.[3] Women don't generally create wars, do we? We build communities rather than destroy them. We bring people together rather than drive them apart. We're motivated by ensuring the world will be a nice place in which future generations can grow and prosper.

I know that with more women in global positions of power and influence, the world can be a kinder, gentler place. Women, especially us wise, older ones, can create that world. But we often shrink back because we've accepted the negative nonsense about being an older woman. I believe there's never been a better time to revolutionize the way we—and the world—view women in the second half of our lives. It's time for us to step into and own our midlife magnificence, so we can feel fulfilled and make the impact we're being called to make. To step forward, not step back.

So please, come with me on a magnificent midlife journey. Let's make your midlife magnificent and get you living the life you really want to live. And then, let's change the world!

We'll start with changing yours.

HOW TO USE THIS BOOK

This book is a mix of research-based facts with action-oriented tips and suggestions from my life and the lives of others. I'm not a doctor and am not providing medical advice. I'm sharing information I've learnt about midlife and menopause that I've found useful and that I hope will help you.

The book is designed to be read in order from beginning to end. It's a practical guide to transforming your life now and into the future. There are questions at the end of each chapter, which I encourage you to answer as you go along, to process your thoughts and feelings as you move through the book. I suggest you get yourself a nice new journal so you can write stuff down and reference later on.

Part One of the book sets the scene by examining the negative narratives about midlife, aging, and menopause that I aim to dispel. It will help you start creating new narratives about yourself, where you are in life now, and what's available for you. Part Two is specifically about managing your menopause transition, where I share what I've discovered to help you thrive through it, not just survive. The need for hormonal balance is life long, so even if you're through menopause, I hope you'll still find this section useful. If you're struggling with menopause issues now and need immediate help, you could jump straight to Part Two.

Part Three is where you get to build your magnificent future. You'll be guided through a process similar to what I use with my mentoring clients, to start crafting a next chapter that will light you up long term. If you're already totally sorted on the hormonal balance side of life, you could read Part One and then jump to Part Three.

You can find additional free resources at magnificentmidlife.com/bookresources

Welcome to your magnificent midlife and beyond! Help me change the world, one magnificent midlife woman at a time! Yes, that means you, Magnificent One.

Rachel x

PART I

CRISIS, WHAT CRISIS?
UNPICKING OLD NARRATIVES

CHAPTER ONE

TIME FOR A NEW PERSPECTIVE ON MIDLIFE

"I choose to make the rest of my life the best of my life."
Louise Hay

HAVING YOUR CAKE AND EATING IT TOO

Since I started writing about menopause and midlife in 2015, a lot has changed, and women are beginning to wake up. Menopause is no longer a word whispered in dark corners. It's out in the open and demands to be heard. Back then, I felt like a lone voice. When early menopause hit me in 2007, there were few resources. Now there's much more being spoken about menopause in all its guises.

The UK has been leading the discussion, and women in other countries are starting to wonder why more isn't being done where they are. An early exception to this pattern was the wonderful US *Menopodcast*, which latterly featured me talking about initiatives in the UK! The US is (at the time of this writing) ahead of the UK when it comes to considering the needs of lactating mothers in the workplace but is still seriously lagging on menopause awareness and action. In other countries, there's even less discussion. It's clear there's a lot of work to be done worldwide on raising awareness about menopause.

If you search *#menopause* on Twitter, you'll find an army of women eager to talk. From a campaign for posters in doctors' offices, to awareness-raising programs in the workplace, to getting menopause on the curriculum in schools (so sex education no longer ends with childbirth), to discussions to protect menopausal women in the workplace—menopause is definitely having a moment.

And yet, midlife is about much more than just menopause. If you think of midlife as a cake, I want menopause to be just one (or maybe two) slices of that cake, not the whole damn cake. Depending on your experience of menopause, that could mean midlife is not a very tasty cake! It would also be overwhelming, which I do not want for you, unless, of course, you've already completely and utterly embraced the wonderful transformative side of menopause. Then you can have as much magical menopause in your midlife cake as you like. I'll be talking a lot about menopause here because it's a big part of midlife, and it needs to be talked about more. But there's also so much more to us midlife women than just how we go through menopause. This book will seek to redress the balance and make menopause a less overwhelmingly negative (and culpable) part of the whole.

FROM AGEISM TO POSITIVE AGING

There's also a shift occurring in how women adjust to midlife and the aspirations we have for our second half. We're starting to be more aware of the impact of ageism and how, when mixed with sexism, it creates an insidious combination that impacts everything. This combination makes it difficult for women over 45 to get or stay in work, let alone feel good about ourselves and life in general. We're beginning to realize that just because it's always been that way doesn't mean it always has to be that way. I think we have the baby boomers to thank for this. They've done much to change the narrative about what to expect from life. They're not going to sit back and accept the status quo as they become our elder generation.

The work of Ashton Applewhite[4] has been instrumental in making me start banging the anti-ageism drum. When I felt catapulted by early menopause into middle age at 41, it was a while before I twigged that I was being ageist towards myself. Of course, I was middle aged! With average life expectancy of 81 for women in the UK, I was smack bang in the middle of my life. Clearly, I hope to live to 100, but that's not especially realistic. I was certainly, at 41, at the beginning of my midlife years. As I write this at 55, I think I'm now well into the second half of my midlife years. Ashton's Ted Talk, "Let's End Ageism,"[5] and her book, *This Chair Rocks*,[6] were life-changing for me. She turns all our accepted truisms about aging completely on their collective head.

Ageism begins between our ears, says Ashton. It starts with the narratives going round in our heads. These have been learned throughout lifetimes of inherent ageism focused particularly on women, such as messages to cover up gray hair, buy useless products to hold back wrinkles and age-spots, and undergo injections and surgery to hold back the "ravages" of time. No judgment if this works for you, but I ask why we so often feel the need to do all this? Why are visible signs of aging wrong for a woman? No thought or desire ever materializes in isolation; propaganda is very effective. Our beliefs are the product of our learning and experiences. Like children who don't see skin color until it's pointed out to them, women probably wouldn't care about the natural changes that come with age if we weren't fed a constant narrative from birth that aging is bad, we're in a slow decline, and youth is superior to everything.

When early menopause struck, it was this internal ageism that caused me the most angst. I'd bought into all the negative narratives about aging. I'd tried the anti-aging creams. I thought I was better than older women. I'm ashamed to admit I dismissed women at work who were the age I am now. In the office, I didn't consider them, not that there were that many of them around anyway in the very male dominated world in which I worked. They'd all sensibly moved on, I reckon.

I believed the birthday cards that say aging is a downward slope, that young people are the ones with energy and bright ideas, that older women are less relevant and valuable. To be forced to cope with being postmenopausal at least 10 years earlier than usual was a huge shock to my system. I struggled against it for quite a while. Being postmenopausal just didn't tally with how I saw myself. As I started questioning everything about myself, I also started questioning the status quo. I realized the assumptions I had made in no way reflected how I felt about where I was in life. I was just getting started. I was just finding my power, not losing it. Nobody was going to dismiss me as past it!

The COVID-19 pandemic brought ageism in all its ugliness to the fore. We saw some governments initially considering it potentially acceptable to discount older people as less valuable than younger people. When considering how best to tackle the pandemic, some in power wanted to ignore the greater susceptibility to the virus of older people or those already unwell, in favor of maintaining the freedom of the young and healthy. If we accept that we cannot discriminate according to race, why is it still acceptable to do that with age? Or level of general health? When did we get the power to decide who is most valuable? Isn't that what we fought a world war over? If we shout about other forms of social injustice, why is ageism still an acceptable form of prejudice?

Toxic narratives

The idea of *anti-aging* (how I hate that phrase!) is finally losing some of its power too. Women start buying anti-aging products in their 20s, or even younger. What's that about? The marketing from cosmetics brands, which make money from fueling our insecurity, can be relentless. I think being anti-aging is about as sensible as being anti-nighttime. It's not going to get you very far. I want us to be pro-aging or age-positive. We also need to change our perception of beauty, not give it an age cutoff. I hear women talk of the perfection of youth and how they are, therefore, now less than perfect. I say, "rubbish!" We are perfect exactly how we are: big, small, old, young, all colors, all shapes, and all sizes. We don't discount the beauty of autumn leaves in favor of spring blossom. Each is beautiful, just different from the other. Our beauty doesn't diminish as we age; it evolves.

This book is a rallying cry for all of us to rewrite the toxic ageist narratives that surround us. It's a clarion call for us to embrace who we are in our entire midlife splendor and get ready for our exciting next chapter. I want you to believe anything is possible—that we can remain vibrant, sexy, relevant, beautiful women until the day we die. Because that's who we are. And that if we can fully step into our power, we and the world will benefit immensely.

The end of my fertility has become the most fertile time of my life. When we're done making babies, we're ready to solve problems. This truth applies to all women, whether or not we've had children because, as we'll explore, post-menopause, we're different. We have a different hormonal profile, different aspirations, and different desires. We've been told that's a negative change. I invite you to set old preconceptions aside as we explore together how wonderful we and our lives can be, in midlife and beyond.

I'm delighted to see there's a groundswell of support for the positive aging movement now too. There are rumblings of discontent from women now deeply into middle age who refuse to accept they're any less relevant because they're daring to get older. Many of us have got used to having it all—or at least trying to—and nobody is going to tell us to go sit quietly in a corner any time soon.

FINDING OUR VOICES

Women can have great power when we unite and find our voices. The Women's March of December 2017, galvanized after the election of President Trump and the #metoo movements, showed us that especially. I joined the Women's March in Washington. It was wonderful to see women of all ages walking together with a collective voice. We may not all agree on how these kinds of protests take place or how movements develop. Still, despite inherent issues of white privilege or class, it's important to recognize there's great power in a collective female voice.

I believe we find a more challenging voice as we get older and that we often get more radical with age. Is that happening to you? We often tend to care less about what may have stopped us when we were younger. As we age, we find the voice that may have been muffled for decades. I also believe menopause and our changing hormones have a role to play in this. (I'll talk more about that later). Jane Fonda has always been ready to fight for her beliefs. At 80, she moved to Washington DC and gets arrested regularly participating in climate change protests. Not something most of us could feasibly do (yet), but I love her tenacity!

The #metoo movement has also made us question more around what's acceptable and what's not. Things to which society once turned a blind eye now face the glare of publicity. Women are no longer willing to accept a status quo dictated by the patriarchy. There's a growing awareness that we can all make a difference, whatever our background or age. The pandemic and the overdue resurgence of the Black Lives Matter movement in 2020 highlighted discrimination and injustice in all their forms. When one group's rights are threatened, all our rights are threatened.

I see more people (and women especially) willing to speak up now. We are coming forward more, and especially as we age. I hope this increased awareness of the need for social justice will have a positive effect across the board. If we needed a sign that older women must find their voices and speak up, I believe the combination of all these factors means that time is NOW. The world is changing, and we are too. The world needs the wisdom of us mature women. It's time we recognized our innate power. We can have so much impact on our own lives and the world, if we trust the voice we find in midlife and speak up.

CHECK-IN

Write down the answers to these questions in your notebook or journal.

- What are your beliefs about aging and menopause?
- Do you know where those beliefs came from?
- Do you feel you need to cover up signs of aging, and if so, why?
- In what ways can you see your personal value has increased over time?
- What's one thing you're passionate about that you're willing to speak up about now?

CHAPTER TWO

CHALLENGING THE ESTABLISHED NORMS ABOUT AGING

*"Aging is not lost youth but a new stage
of opportunity and strength."*
Betty Friedan

WHAT WE LEARN ABOUT AGING

So much of what we've learned to accept about midlife and aging is utter rubbish. It took me going through early menopause to wake up to the fact that women have been sold a load of nonsense when it comes to getting older.

This negativity exists mainly because there's such a big gulf in our society's (specifically men's) perception of a fertile woman and an infertile one. We go through life learning that youth is best and that only the young are beautiful, sexy, creative, full of energy and so on, and we associate those things with fertility. We find a mate by being our most attractive. Many of us compete with other women to be the most alluring mate for men. Because of this link between youth, vibrancy, beauty, and fertility, the idea of moving from being fertile to no longer fertile often fills us with dread. What is our role as an infertile woman? Where do we fit in? So much of a woman's identity is wrapped up in her ability to reproduce (even if she doesn't have children) that when that physical ability goes, many of us don't know who we are any more. And we often have a very negative perception of who we are now. That's certainly how I felt, even though childbearing was only part of who I was. I walked out of that doctor's office feeling ancient, that the best of my life was over. I let the diagnosis of menopause instantly change who I believed I was. How sad was I, thinking that? But I had no idea who I was post menopause. What was I supposed to do, think, feel? Who was I now, and what was left for me?

It's acceptable for men to get older. There are few negative associations around men aging. They become silver foxes. They don't become invisible when they have wrinkles and gray hair. Their stature increases rather than diminishes as they age. And, of course, the ultimate injustice: they can continue to reproduce until the day they die (well, technically, anyway). Nick Nolte, Clint Eastwood, and Rod Stewart all sired a child at 66, and Mick Jagger was 73.[7] But not us women. Not only do our eggs have a use by date, but we're also taught to be ashamed of and cover up the signs of aging. We're sold anti-aging products all our lives. Older male actors are paired with women half their age in movies. Older male TV presenters can roll out of bed and into the TV studio, but not their female counterparts. The latter need hours in hair and makeup, and to be dyed, nipped and tucked to within an inch of their lives.

We're made to feel shame for every wrinkle, sunspot or gray hair. We get the Botox, the facelifts, the hair dye. And we contribute to making older women invisible because we're not looking the way nature meant us to look at this time of life. We may believe it's what we want and that we're exercising freedom of choice. If you want Botox, go for it. However, I'd argue that the decision to get Botox isn't just yours alone; you're not making it in isolation. If you decide you want it, it's likely because it's what you've been taught to want.

You've been taught to view your aging face a certain way, and I want to challenge that assumption. I see wrinkles as the maps of our lives. I've earned mine! Crow's feet show we've smiled a lot. I've also frowned a fair bit too (the lines between my eyebrows remind me of that), but that's okay. What sunspots I have remind me that, even living in rainy old England most of my life, I've enjoyed the warmth of the sun on my face too. We may look more tired as we age, but even that's a personal judgment. Consider also that it's possible we aren't aware of the subconscious reasons we choose to change our looks. You've been taught that visibly aging skin is bad, or at least not as good as young skin. You've been taught to view your own face as less attractive if it shows signs of age or even just looks tired as you perceive it.

I have a confession to make here. As well as actually appreciating my wrinkles, I don't dye my hair and never will. Apart from a few white hairs at the front, my hair still has its original color, just a bit lighter. My mother at 87 is strawberry blond rather than the bright auburn she was when younger. She moans about how she's lost a lot of color. I tell her not to be so daft. Even though I'm not currently losing hair color, I like to think that if I did, I'd embrace it. I know many women prefer to cover their gray or white hair, but I think the way our hair changes color as we age suits our older skin tone.

Gray and white hair can look stunning. You've only got to look at the gorgeous British silver curve model Rachel Peru[8] to see that. She didn't become a model until she stopped using hair dye and let her natural hair color shine through. You can listen to her story on my Magnificent Midlife Podcast.[9]

Of course, it's a matter of personal choice, but, like the Botox, I'd argue the decision to cover silver hair isn't a choice freely made because we're inundated with messages that older women aren't beautiful, vibrant, or sexy. We're told that having natural silver hair ages us, and if we look older, we'll be sidelined. We suffer ageism everywhere and particularly at work, where sexism enjoys having a friend to hang out with. Many women feel they have to cover up aging hair, in particular, to stay visible and relevant in the workplace and so they don't disappear to those around them or those in authority. We can be subject to this prejudice at home too. Menfolk who are perfectly happy to go gray themselves can sometimes pressure their partners to keep the dye. I know one woman whose husband is happy to dye her hair himself, rather than let it become the natural color it is. This seems rather sad to me. Even when the husband is himself older, he doesn't want the world to see him with an older-looking woman. We can't win, can we?

The marketing and advertising industries, and most importantly, the clients they serve, play a huge role in perpetuating the myth that youth is the best stage of life. They make a lot of money by cultivating our insecurities and promoting misogynistic myths and stereotypes. There's so much money to be made from hair dye, anti-aging products,

Botox, face-lifts, and stay-younger-longer treatments. Just imagine if all women, as I used to, purchase anti-aging products constantly from age 20, for life! We also tend to try out the more expensive ones as we get older and perhaps have more money available, just to see if the claims are true. Try doing the calculation on your own spending, then multiply it by billions. The global anti-aging market was estimated to be worth US$44 billion in 2021 and predicted to be worth US$58 billion by 2026.[10] That's a national economy right there, predicated on the myth that signs of female aging need to be hidden. Many companies have a lot invested in maintaining these myths. (Not to mention those companies working to persuade women they need to take hormones for life; but we'll get to that particular soapbox of mine later.)

"Youth is best" messages keep us as the captive buying audience. Remember how smoking used to be so cool we all wanted to do it? We finally woke up to the truth behind that marketing campaign. Youth is when we're smarter, quicker and most attractive, right? No, I believe we're smarter, at least in terms of the stuff we know, and potentially just as quick and attractive, as we progress through life. A perfect body is a young one, correct? No, a perfect body is one that functions in good health and allows us to do everything we want to do. Youth doesn't mysteriously bestow some magical luster of beauty or perfection. We've just been brainwashed to believe it does.

Being a bit older doesn't change who you fundamentally are. It doesn't lessen you in any way. I'd argue age can make women more attractive, not less. I see great beauty in older women's faces, as our character sets in and our bone structure becomes more defined. I believe my mother is still beautiful at 87, and also that her most "typically" attractive decade was her 50s, when she really grew into her features. Our beauty doesn't diminish as we age; it evolves. One of the most beautiful women I've ever met was the incredible yogi, Tao Porchon-Lynch,[11] who sadly died at age 101. I met her when she was 99. The beauty that radiated out of her was unlike anything I've ever seen, utterly breathtaking and infectious. Her smile was a sight to behold. I'd been a fan for several years when I finally met her in the flesh. I was so overwhelmed, I cried, soft melt that I am! To me, she was the essence of true beauty.

SEEING AGING IN A POSITIVE LIGHT

We're told not only that our looks are in terminal decline, but also that life in general is downhill from 30, 40, 50. The narrative is that getting older means physical, mental, and emotional decline. What if we turn that narrative on its head, too? Apart from the very end of life, there's no reason to view aging as decline. There are lots of examples of older people living long, healthy, vibrant lives well past midlife. I was fitter than I'd ever been at age 50 when I completed my first half marathon. Clearly some older people are the exception rather than the rule, and many of us can't aspire to be as fit as them. Nevertheless, we don't have to accept the prevailing narrative that it's all a downward slope into ill-health, reduced mobility, and ever-diminishing value. A lot of it depends on how we approach the second half and the extent to which we look after ourselves, physically and emotionally (we'll get to this later). I believe the first half is just the rehearsal. Midlife is when life starts to get really interesting. I know of so many women who've listened to the call of their itchy feet and found their true inspiration and joy in the second half. I want that for you too.

Tao was a perfect example of a woman determined to squeeze every last drop out of life. She didn't start ballroom dancing until she was in her 80s and went on to dance on *America's Got Talent*[12] at 96! Just because we may not be able to achieve lotus position after three hip replacements in our 90s (like Tao) doesn't mean there isn't lots else we can do. I think there can be a tendency to look at the super-agers and feel we can't compete, so we don't try anything much. Perfectionism can stop us from even starting something. We think, *if I can't be perfect or age perfectly, why bother making an effort?* But it's always worth the effort.

Aging well comes down to how we choose to live our lives. Only about 25% of how we age is due to our genes. The rest is up to us.[13] Even if we've lived the first half not looking after ourselves, that's no reason to give up now. In fact, it's even more of a reason to take back control in the next chapter. Did you know we can build muscle mass in our 90s? As we'll cover later in this book, midlife is the perfect time to invest in making sure our health is best positioned to allow us to live a long and healthy life. We can absolutely make up for lost time.

Research has also shown that how we feel about aging[14] affects our experience of it. The more we fear it, the faster we age, both physically and mentally. Remember the old adage, mind over matter? When it comes to how well we age, it's crucial. Aging isn't a problem to be fixed or denied.

The movement for "conscious aging" wants us to be aware of and accept what aging is—a notice that life has a beginning, a middle and an end—and to eliminate the denial that means we don't get to enjoy what may turn out to be the most joyful time of our lives. If we see age as limiting us and we accept those limitations, you can be absolutely certain we will "age" accordingly.

Midlife malaise

I'd argue that the way dissatisfaction can hit us in midlife is also all mixed up with how society views aging in general. This bit impacts men just as much as women. We're entering a stage of life that we've been taught to believe makes us officially "old," or at least, way past "young." Big birthdays can compound that feeling. When approaching big birthdays, we often spend time assessing what we've achieved up to that point in life. Our natural predisposition towards focusing on the negative and wallowing in status anxiety can lead us quickly to the assumption that we're a long way off from where we "should" be in life. Then we can start to feel really bad about ourselves, get stuck in the midlife crisis loop, and hunker down in those terminal decline stories. No! But then what is our coping strategy? Some of us try to pretend it's not happening and deny, deny, deny. However, as I mentioned already, accepting and then embracing aging is actually at the heart of aging well.

HOW OLD ARE YOU, REALLY?

Many people say they don't feel their age. There's evidence that feeling either younger or older than you are (your subjective age[15]) has a strong effect on your physical and mental health. The effect is good if you feel younger and bad if you feel older than your actual age. Why is this so? It's not just positive thinking if you feel younger. It's also linked to disliking your age or judgment that you're doing better, or not so well, compared to where others are in life. In reality, you can only actually feel the true age that you are. Whether you feel 20, 30, 40, or 75 in your head is immaterial. What's important is whether you feel positive about the age you are. There's also an element of age denial in claiming to feel younger than you are. Younger is better, right? It's good to feel younger than your age. But why do we think that?

If we believe aging is a good thing, we're happy to feel the age we really are. It took me a while to get to this point in accepting aging, but it makes perfect sense to me now. I believe my age is the sum total of all that I am. I may feel good, healthy, and energetic for my actual age, but not younger than it. Why would I feel younger than I am? How can I know that to be true, anyway? Conceptually that just doesn't work for me. Neither do rigid ideas of what any particular age looks or behaves like either. We're all unique, and we all age differently.

In fact, we get more diverse, not less, the older we get, which is why lumping everybody in one big 40, 45, 50+ age group, as so often happens, can be so damaging. I hate the way the European Union describes the Silver Economy as everyone over 50.[16] It's a lazy classification and adds to prejudice, I believe. Putting everyone from 50 to 100+ into one categorization bucket, for whatever purpose, makes no sense. The needs, interests and purchases of a 50-year-old are going to be so very different from those of a 90-year-old. Even amongst people we might consider very old, there is huge diversity. Tao Porchon-Lynch was definitely not your typical 101-year-old! In her 90s, she insisted on wearing high heels everywhere and told a fun story of wearing them up Machu Picchu. She was wearing high heels when I met her. This diversity in aging is why geriatricians like to say, "if you've seen one 80-year-old, you've seen one 80-year-old."

Ashton Applewhite says:

"Chronological age tells you almost nothing about an individual—not what they're listening to or who they're voting for or where they're headed—and the older the person, the less reliable an indicator it becomes."[17]

You wouldn't expect two 20-year-olds to be the same, yet we so often set that expectation for older generations.[18] Such lazy age categorizations are everywhere. Next time you get asked to fill in your age on a survey, and it tries to lump you into one over 40, 50 or 60 age bracket, draw a big line through it and state your actual age. Can you imagine if they tried to lump everyone *under* 40 into one age group? That's a preposterous notion, isn't it? How can you lump a teenager in with a 30 year old? And yet society tries to do that with older people all the time. It's all part of the way society devalues us past an acceptable age.

HOW DO YOU WANT TO AGE?

The way people are perceived to age has certainly changed since I was young. My parents were "older" when they were a lot younger than my generation. My father saw himself as old in his 60s. He allowed the number of years he'd been alive to dictate his behavior and what was and wasn't appropriate for him. Sadly, he also used it as an excuse to slow right down, particularly after very early retirement at 50. He sat down in a chair at 55 and did very little exercise or even regular movement after that.

Unsurprisingly, his life was not an especially long or happy one, and his body finally gave up after a decade of ill health at 75. Observing his experience has greatly influenced my approach to aging and made me want to look after my own health as I go through midlife and into the magnificent beyond. My husband, in his 60s, seems positively boyish in comparison with my dad at the same age. We all have choices, and how much effort we put into aging healthfully is one of the most important ones we can make.

My mum has never been one for much exercise either, but she's a keen gardener, which has always kept her mobile. My husband can spend a day in the garden and do 17,000 steps back and forth (if you're not a step counter like me, that's a lot). My mum listens to my healthy aging sermons and goes to a regular Pilates class, but exercise is not something that comes instinctively to her. I've learnt that staying active is one of the most important aspects of keeping ourselves healthy, both physically and mentally, as we age.

As Ashton says, ageism begins between our ears. If we don't want to be pigeonholed, we shouldn't start doing it to ourselves. So don't put yourself in any box! Don't assume there are things you can no longer do. Make the choice to age well. If you catch yourself thinking you're too old to do this or too old to wear that, ask yourself where that idea came from. Is it just another load of rubbish you can ignore? Choice applies to your thoughts just as much as to your actions. We'll look more at this idea throughout this book. Remember, you are never too old, and it is never too late!

CHECK-IN

Write down the answers to these questions in your notebook or journal.

- How can you learn to love your wrinkles?
- Think of a few beautiful older women. What about them inspires you?
- What age do you feel? Is it older, younger or the same as your actual age?
- Do you sometimes think you're too old to do something? How can you reframe that idea?
- How do you compare with your parents in terms of how you are aging?

CHAPTER THREE

FINDING INSPIRATION FOR CHANGING BELIEFS

"Midlife is not a crisis. Midlife is an unravelling."
Brené Brown

THE U-CURVE OF HAPPINESS

Another myth about midlife and aging is that we get more and more unhappy the older we get. We really don't. There's truth in the idea that midlife can be an unhappy time, but specifically which part of midlife? If we assume a low average life expectancy of 80 (in the US and Europe, at least) and we think of life as having three acts, you might consider that midlife is the period from 40-60. I sure as hell was unhappy in my early 40s, but now in my mid-50s, life is much brighter. I wish that for you too.

The idea of the midlife crisis is deeply ingrained in our collective psyche. You only have to turn to Google and type in "midlife," and the first thing that comes up is "crisis." Of course, it's all downhill from there! Like Brené Brown, I believe that rather than being a crisis, midlife is much more a time of reckoning and re-evaluation. It's when we need to take time to reflect, unpack who we are now, and re-connect with who we are becoming. Big birthdays, as we've seen, can add to this inclination towards introspection in midlife.

I believe it's a time when you may feel a desperate pull to live the life you want, not necessarily the one you've ended up with. That's one reason why we often feel so unsure of ourselves in midlife, when we can be plagued with self-doubt and itchy feet. That reassessment of what we've done with our life so far, and pondering where to go next, surfaces around a major life reckoning point. Midlife is the ultimate reckoning point for many; I'm here to rebrand it as a magnificent opportunity, rather than a crisis.

During your midlife unraveling, you can take further solace in the U-curve of happiness.[19] It's been scientifically proven that we're happiest at the beginnings and ends of our lives with a big dip in the middle like a letter U. Research shows that 47[20] is our unhappiest age, the depths of midlife malaise. If you're feeling down in midlife, the U-curve of happiness is there to back you up and pull you forward. Things will, for most of us, get better in the happiness stakes as life goes on.

There may be nothing in particular making you unhappy; it's just a natural phase of life. It's the middle that can get us down simply because it's the middle. Feelings of discontent, restlessness, and even sometimes worthlessness are not unexpected. The big birthday soul-searching can make it all the worse. We're still tied to those outdated ideas of what we should and shouldn't have achieved by any particular age, forgetting, as we are wont to do, that we all have different lives and are on different trajectories. Comparison is the thief of joy. (If I ever get a tattoo, it may well say that.) I don't want you to fall into the trap of midlife malaise like I did for a while. There are many steps you can take to make this the most magical time of your life, so far.

If your 40s are a bit gloomy, there's every chance that around 50, the fog will begin to lift. There are clearly other factors that may prevent that outcome, but all things being equal, that's the normal trajectory of life. The U-curve holds. Sometimes a little knowledge can be so powerful. I wish I'd known about the U-curve of happiness when I was in the pit of my struggles in the first half of my 40s. How much easier it would have been if I could have stopped beating myself up about feeling bad and embraced this natural transition then. Now that I know about the U-curve, I'm even more excited about the years to come.

Midlife unhappiness is also often exacerbated by anxiety and denial around the very idea of being in midlife itself. We've already looked at how denial can be a coping strategy, though not a particularly good one. Anxiety and denial can be attributed to our fear of getting really old eventually. We don't want to acknowledge there's a shorter road ahead of us than the one we've already walked, or that the clock is ticking down. Facing our own mortality, perhaps for the first time, can be a big shock. But by embracing the finite nature of life, you can make the most of the many good years you still have. What a waste to spend our later years worrying about possible difficulties much later on. Getting very old, and even the end of life, may turn out to be absolutely fine after all.

If you'd like to get a handle on precisely how much time you may have left, there are several Life/Death Clocks[21] on the Internet. Yes, I know that sounds really weird, but they can be very helpful. You plug in your current age, gender, and general health condition, and you'll get an idea of your life expectancy. Clearly, the result is all down to an algorithm, and it may sound a bit scary, but I found doing the exercise to be pretty empowering. It was certainly an important step in making me get my act together, sort out my lifestyle, and start making the most of the time I have left. My life expectancy goes up dramatically, by the way, if I take alcohol out of my qualifying criteria. Who knows what the exact science is behind these online tools, but I like the concept. Any personal experience of death often has the effect of making us want to squeeze every last drop out of life. We may all die tomorrow if the universe decides it will be so. The COVID-19 pandemic brought that home to the world like nothing else.

As we've seen, it's easy to believe the negative narratives around midlife, menopause, and aging. It's a tough job to escape years of conditioning. This conditioning is especially true for women because, as we've seen, sexism kicks in to give ageism its own special tinge. For many white heterosexual men, ageism is often the first prejudice they encounter, and it can come as a big shock. Only then do many of them start to develop more understanding of the kind of prejudice other societal groups have to face throughout life.

It's also often easier to keep believing what appears to be a universal truth than to challenge it. It takes real effort to decide to turn your back on that truth and start creating your own narrative. But we can find inspiration for this fight-back in the experience of older people in other cultures around the world.

AGEISM AND THE WEST

Newsflash: *Western aging norms are not universal!* Yes, really! Getting older, and older people themselves, are viewed very differently depending on where you are in the world. Even within Western nations, there are huge differences in how societies view aging and their older populations. Arianna Huffington has written in her book *On Becoming Fearless*[22] about how old age is honored and celebrated in Greece. Elders take pride of place in the family. Abbotts and abbesses are addressed as "Old Man" and "Old Woman," terms of deep respect not dismissal.

I long had a theory that there's something particular about Anglo-Saxon culture that worships youth. I see this most acutely in the US, UK, and Australia. I had no idea why this was the case, but while researching for this book, I found an article[23] that suggests my own youth-centric British culture, emphasizing attributes such as individualism and independence, has its roots in Protestantism. This viewpoint relates to the Protestant work ethic, which ties an individual's value to her or his ability to work, something that is thought to diminish with age. This philosophy doesn't appear to have moved with the times (or with increased life expectancy), not to mention improvements in long-term physical health and the length of time many older people are still in work.

This link to Protestantism could explain why we don't tend to see the same degree of ageism in Western countries that do not have Protestant history, such as Italy, France, Greece, and Spain. In these countries, older people, and older women especially, appear to have more status than in my own.

AGING IN OTHER CULTURES

When talking about aging and older people globally, it's often cited that East Asian cultures have more respect for their older people than does the West. People also don't feel the same negativity about aging in those cultures because people don't lose status or respect as they get older. Confucianism and its focus on filial piety is often quoted as the motivation for greater respect for age in China, Korea, and Japan, for example. I've spent time in China and can vouch for the greater level of innate deference to older people there. In my 20s, if a Chinese man or woman was more than five or so years older than me, I would always address them with some honorific title. In a work context, this would be their actual work title. Socially, it would be "Auntie" or "Uncle," whether or not there was any blood relation. It came as quite a shock when I started getting addressed as Auntie myself! At a family meal, the oldest members are always given the best seats, facing the door, and their well-being is always the priority.

There are still many sons (and daughters) in China bringing up their own families while living with their parents, as was the traditional way. This situation is changing after the combination of the one-child policy in the 1980s, the resulting one grandchild, the ever-increasing cost of living, and pressures on younger people to advance their careers. But how older people are treated in China is still very different from their treatment in many parts of the West. In an effort to maintain these traditions in a changing world (and push back responsibility onto families rather than the state), China introduced the Elderly Rights Law under which children have to visit their parents frequently, no matter how far away they live. If not, they could face fines or even jail. Interestingly, France (a historically Catholic country) also passed a law in 2004, which requires adult children to "keep in touch" with their parents. It was apparently passed in response to a study[24] showing a high rate of elderly suicides in France, as well as to a heat wave in 2003, in which 15,000 mostly elderly people died.

In Korea and Japan, many older adults also live with their adult children, and big celebrations are held around birthdays. In Korea, 60th and 70th birthdays[25] are celebrated in high style, as reaching these ages is still seen as something their ancestors would not have achieved. In Japan, the 60th birthday, Kanreki, is considered very important and a cause for great celebration. Turning 60 is thought of as rebirth, as you have passed five times through the traditional 12-year lunar calendar zodiac and returned to your birth sign. Sadly, as in the West, Japanese women often prefer to keep their 60th birthday quiet while the men celebrate. Double standards in force again. I must do a Japanese edition of this book!

One fascinating study from Löckenhoff et al,[26] looked at 26 cultures and corroborated the East-West differences in perceptions of aging but also found interesting differences. The study shows lots of different variables at play when it comes to how aging is viewed, including perceived attractiveness, ability to do everyday tasks, wisdom, received respect, and family authority, among others.

"Broad East-West comparisons found a small but significant effect, indicating that participants from Asian cultures do indeed hold more positive societal views of aging than their Western counterparts. However, this effect was qualified by the finding that participants from Asian cultures show less favorable perceptions of changes in wisdom."

Even if you're thought to grow less mentally astute in Asia, that doesn't impact how much respect you receive.

In Indian cultures around the world, elders are heads of the family and play an important role in raising children, often with several generations all under one roof. The opinions of older people are sought after, and their word is often final in settling disputes.[27] An Indian woman may not like aging, but she doesn't usually have to fear losing status. In cultures where bigger families are more common, the role of older people is often crucial in bringing up the next generation; hence, their perceived value doesn't diminish. In traditional hunter-gatherer societies, which still exist in some parts of the world, older women are often greatly respected. They know where the good food can be found, what's poisonous, how to manage conflict in communities, and more. Their wisdom and experience are of great value.

Like the Auntie and Uncle titles in China, we also find respect for older people reflected in other languages. In Hindi the use of the suffix *ji* enables speakers to pay more respect to another person, often older. The word *mzee*[28] in Kiswahili, spoken in many parts of Africa, is used by younger speakers to give older people respect; and the Haiwaiian word *kūpuna*[29] plays a similar role. But there seems to be a preponderance of disrespectful or patronizing terms to refer to older people, and especially women, in English speaking countries.

Something else I discovered is that as we get richer, we seem to disparage aging more. The study above also found that despite the role of filial piety in Japanese culture, Japan's perceptions of aging now place closer to those in the US and UK. It surmised this was partly due to Japan's much greater proportion of older people and its ever-diminishing birth rate, putting more perceived pressure on caring for older Japanese. This seeming correlation between so-called progress and devaluing older people is a theme I am keen to challenge.

I'm sharing all this because I want you to question your thoughts about aging and consider alternatives. I've learned that just because you think something doesn't make it true. Similarly, just because you've always accepted something and it's ingrained in your psyche, doesn't make it true either. Your thoughts and beliefs are the product of your upbringing and the culture in which you live. If you think of it like that, you can change any narrative and belief system just by approaching it from a different angle. I'll be asking you to do more work on challenging your beliefs, both about yourself and the world, as you progress through this book.

In the next chapter, we'll look at how society's beliefs about menopause, in particular, need a refresh. In fact, a complete rebrand of this important transition in women's lives is long overdue! Like aging, I believe there are a lot more positive elements of menopause than we are led to believe.

CHECK-IN

Write down the answers to these questions in your notebook or journal.

- Where would you place yourself on the U-curve of happiness right now?
- What lies ahead that you look forward to?
- Which country's treatment of older women is most appealing to you? Why?
- How can you bring some of those ideas into your own life?
- What positive descriptions can you start using about yourself in this stage of life?

CHAPTER FOUR

REBRANDING MENOPAUSE

*"The menopausal woman is the prisoner of a
stereotype and will not be rescued from it until
she has begun to tell her own story."*
Germaine Greer

CULTURE AGAIN

I started this book telling you about my fear of being a
dried-up old prune at 41. What little I knew about menopause was overwhelmingly negative, and I'd bought into the
narrative that menopause was the end of meaningful life.
I didn't do that for very long, thank goodness, but it was
the first unpleasant thought to hit me as I left the doctor's
office.

As with aging in general, culture matters massively when it
comes to how we understand, approach, and experience
menopause. It's not just a physical experience, as we'll
explore later. And how we each experience menopause is
unique, dependent on many factors, including geography.
I find it fascinating that women in Western English-speak-
ing cultures, where I've noticed the most ageism, appear
to report the most angst about menopause and the worst

menopause-related issues. One study[30] found that British women reported the very worst symptoms.

"It may be that symptoms experienced during the menopausal transition arise through a complexity of factors, and not simply declining levels of estrogen; ethnicity, geographic location, stress, local culture and age are factors that also need to be taken into account."

If we take a quick gander through the experience of other cultures, we see how there is often a correlation between how aging in general is perceived and women's experience of menopause. In China, menopause is called a woman's "second spring," and anecdotal evidence suggests menopause is less of an issue for women in China. Obviously, there are lots of aspects to consider, such as how taboo the subject is, diet, body weight, environment, levels of exercise, and so on, which we'll discuss later. But I fundamentally believe that if we don't fear getting older so much, we will also feel less fear around menopause. And if we don't fear menopause, our experience of it can often be easier. We may even look forward to the time when we're no longer a slave to estrogen, which has made us want to nurture everyone except ourselves, as we wave a fond goodbye to the emotional roller-coaster of our menstrual cycle. That is my hope for women.

If I were a Native American, I'd have likely viewed the menopausal transition as a neutral or positive experience as I moved to becoming a "woman of wisdom" in my community. Many women in cultures where aging is viewed more positively, or where lack of fertility can be viewed in terms of greater freedom, report few menopausal issues, simply a cessation of periods. Our personal attitude towards menopause has a significant role in our overall experience of it.

We'll look elsewhere at the power of the mind, but starting with the very transition of menopause, what we believe will be, often will be. Our expectations can become self-fulfilling prophecies. Women who have negative attitudes towards menopause and/or aging are more likely to report a greater number and frequency of menopausal symptoms.[31] Western societies, which do not necessarily prioritize procreation, still often place a high value on youthfulness. In these societies, menopause signals loss of youth combined with a perceived loss of sexual attractiveness, and this perception can lead to negative attitudes towards the transition.

NEGATIVE LANGUAGE

We also medicalize menopause with much of our associated language being negative, such as "reproductive or ovarian *failure.*" Words matter enormously, as we're discovering. Much of what we believe in the West about the negative aspects of menopause and so-called hormone deficiency stems from a book published in 1966 by gynecologist Robert A Wilson, called *Feminine Forever.* In this best-selling book, Wilson maintained that menopause was a serious, painful, and crippling estrogen-deficiency disease that should be treated with estrogen replacement therapy to prevent the otherwise inevitable "living decay." He promoted the use of a drug that healthy women would take every day for the rest of their lives, so they could remain feminine forever.

Wilson wrote, "All postmenopausal women are castrates." With HRT, "a woman's breasts and genital organs will not shrivel. She will be much more pleasant to live with and will not become dull and unattractive." I believe misogyny and patriarchy were at the core of this argument. It was necessary for the woman to remain feminine to please her man. And remaining feminine required hormone replacement—forever.

Robert Bazell, in an article on the NBC News website,[32] notes that the most amusing section of this book describes a visit to Wilson's office from a prominent member of the Brooklyn underworld:

"The mobster is sick himself, but he has come for the doctor's help for his wife. 'She's driving me nuts,' the tough guy says. 'She won't fix meals. She lets me get no sleep. She picks on me all the time.' The visitor then displays a .32 automatic and tells Wilson, 'If you don't cure her, I'll kill her.' Wilson calmed the mobster. He accepted the wife as his patient and reported that she responded well to twice-a-week estrogen treatments. Her disposition improved noticeably after three weeks and soon she was very busy taking care of her sick husband."

No wonder estrogen has been described as the "biddable" hormone!

Reporters from *The New Republic* and *The Washington Post* discovered documents revealing that Wilson, who died in 1981, received payment for the book and for speaking tours on its behalf from companies making HRT. Sales of HRT quadrupled in the years around the book's publication.

When HRT became linked to breast cancer later on, women stopped using it in droves. Now that associated risk has been found to be much reduced, HRT is more popular again as a treatment to help with menopause-associated issues.

There is no doubt HRT can help many women, but, as I will show in the next chapter, there are many other more natural ways to help us transition. When I read of women again being advised to take HRT forever for long-term health, I can't help thinking that Wilson's book has had a lingering impact on how we as a society and individually view post-menopausal women. No one can claim that long-term use of HRT is completely safe, at least not for another 20 years. The HRT manufacturers must be delighted at the prospect of every woman taking their drug for life. As with the sales of anti-aging creams and hair dye, just imagine how much money that would involve!

What if, instead of the misogynistic narrative that strikes fear in the hearts of women and our menfolk, there is actually an evolutionary reason for menopause that places women at the top of the totem pole of influence, instead of sliding rapidly to the bottom? What if we can create a whole new narrative for this time in our lives? What if we start to see menopause as a gift that enables us to take stock of the lives we've lived and want to live, so we can let go of what no longer serves us while mining the diamonds to sustain us moving forward? What if menopause actually opens up a whole new world of possibility for you rather than being an end of opportunity?

BEING MORE WHALE

In her book, *Flash Count Diary, a New Story about the Menopause*,33 Darcey Steinke explores the many narratives we have about menopause, unpicking them and gently turning most of them on their heads. She saves the very best for last. Through her menopause journey, she discovers there are two creatures that go through menopause: human females and whales. Female killer whales become the leaders of their pods after menopause. Some have lived 50 additional years after their reproductive ones. These older females are no longer in competition for the reproductive attention of the male whales in the pod and can instead focus on guiding and protecting the whole group for the good of the species.

Darcey becomes fixated with the matriarch of a group of whales living in the northeast Pacific Ocean. This particular whale was known as J2 or "Granny." Darcey even went on a boat trip to try to find Granny. You can hear about her encounter with Granny and how Darcey made me cry while telling me the story on my podcast.[34] The experience shifted everything Darcey felt about her own menopause, and she credits it with changing her experience of even her physical menopausal symptoms. It radically transformed her feelings about the change.

Why have women evolved to go through menopause? There must be a good reason. Perhaps, like whales, when we've gone through menopause, we're more valuable to our communities as leaders than as breeders. Being off that estrogen roller-coaster makes us valuable and relevant in ways we never thought of before. If you consider menopause in those terms, it becomes a lot less scary, perhaps even something to look forward to. No more shriveled up old prune sitting quietly in the corner. We can be striding ahead, leading our tribe, living our best lives, enjoying greater hormonal parity with men (no wonder men may find that scary) and rebalancing the world. How's that for a rebrand!

In the next chapter, we'll look at menopause in depth: what it is, how long it may last, and how to transition vibrantly through it. You'll then know everything you need to help you have as good a menopause transition as possible. I hope you're beginning to see it isn't just something negative to be endured, but a hugely transformational time in your life that can lead to greater and better things. I hope your whole experience of it can be reframed positively and you can pass that on to younger generations so they are also prepared, not scared.

Menopause can be hard for some women. I know that. But I believe lifestyle, diet, and mindset changes can alter the experience for most of us. Going back to my cake analogy, let's just make menopause a couple of slices, at most, of your midlife cake. The next section will show you how to limit its negative impact so you can capitalize on its role as a life-changing catalyst helping you create your magnificent midlife and beyond. Bring it on!

CHECK-IN

Write down the answers to these questions in your notebook or journal.

- How has your view of menopause changed so far from reading this book?
- In what ways do you think your personal cultural environment has impacted how you view menopause?
- What do you think about the menopause narrative in the book *Feminine Forever*?
- In what ways do you feel more positive about the possibilities for you post menopause?
- What can you do to "be more whale" in your day-to-day life?

PART II

EMBRACING MENOPAUSE: MANAGING THE TRANSITION WITH EASE

CHAPTER FIVE

UNDERSTANDING THE HORMONAL CHANGES OF MENOPAUSE

"I have tried to view each menopause symptom as my body requesting me to make healthy changes, to facilitate it finding a new balance."
Tania Dalton

I'm writing this at 55 and have been learning about menopause since 41, so I have lots to tell you about this transition and how you can move through it with greater ease.

As you might expect, my opinion is not exactly in line with the predominant view. There are lots of tips here for maintaining long-term hormonal balance and a discussion of menopause that may differ from most of what you've read or heard elsewhere. Whether you're premenopausal, in the middle, or postmenopausal, I hope you'll learn strategies for yourself as well as some you can pass on to other women.

DEFINING MENOPAUSE AND PERIMENOPAUSE

First, let's review some definitions because most of us get the terminology wrong. When people talk about menopause symptoms, they usually mean perimenopause symptoms. As we've discussed, menopause is just a moment in time. It's one year after your last period if you're over 50 and two years if you're under 50. Perimenopause is the period leading up to menopause. The only real symptom of menopause itself is that we stop having a menstrual bleed, which happens, on average, around the age of 51. It can also happen a lot earlier, as it did with me, or much later. Women can still be menstruating at 60, though that's unusual.

The menopause symptoms we experience before that specific point in time are technically perimenopause symptoms. Before menopause itself, we are perimenopausal rather than menopausal. Perimenopause can last a long time, on average four years, but also sometimes only a few months or much longer. After menopause, we are said to be postmenopausal. In the US, some people use the term "menopausal" to refer to any woman who's gone through menopause and continue to use it for the rest of her life.

By the time many of you reach menopause (the moment in time), those pesky or dreadful (depending on your experience) symptoms, if you're lucky, may already be consigned to history. You may be happily skipping off into a lovely postmenopausal life of liberty, free of PMS (premenstrual syndrome) or a monthly bleed. Hooray!

If you're not there yet, and associated issues continue long after menopause, or if perimenopause is difficult and takes forever, then you need help to get better hormonal balance, both during menopause and after it.

Throughout this book, I mostly use the word menopause, because that's what the world understands. However, it's the whole transition I'm usually talking about.

A SMOOTHER TRANSITION

Before I tell you what you may experience, I'm going to throw out a contentious idea. In Tania Elfersy's article on estrogen theory, "The Wiser Woman," she questions the perceived wisdom that a drop in estrogen during the perimenopausal years *causes* menopause symptoms. She doesn't deny there are symptoms around the time of menopause, but she believes these come about because of a set of circumstances that we need to recognize and deal with rather than being *caused* by menopause itself. She believes that hormonal changes exacerbate existing issues, rather than necessarily causing them. Tania says:

"A drop in estrogen does not cause perimenopause and menopause symptoms to arise. A drop in estrogen creates the conditions that allow symptoms to arise IF a woman is pushing her life away from her innate well-being through elevated levels of stress (first and foremost) and other unhealthy lifestyle choices. So why not change the conditions that allow the symptoms to arise? Well firstly, as we have seen with over half a century of experimenting with hormone therapies, when you change the body's brilliantly balanced ecosystem, results are unpredictable, and women remain burdened by symptoms and even dangerous side-effects. And secondly, because doesn't it make sense that if we happen to move away from our innate well-being, we keep in place the naturally occurring warning systems that let us know we need to move back into balance? Women will only start feeling better at midlife when there is a paradigm shift in the understanding of perimenopause and menopause. This will happen when society as a whole starts understanding the confusion that it created in the relationship between estrogen and perimenopause and menopause symptoms."[35]

Until I read this, I felt like a lone voice in the wilderness. This idea makes total sense to me. It's possible this is a far more accurate description of what goes on for women around menopause than the narrative in which it is a medical condition to be fixed. It also helps explain why women have such radically different experiences of menopause, both in our own communities and across the world.

Tania's explanation of what's potentially going on raises questions about which aspects of modern life (and Western life, which we'll explore later) make our experience of menopause seemingly worse than that of our ancestors. It's not just that we're living longer and talking about it more. In some parts of the world, women lived past menopause hundreds, even thousands, of years ago. In her book, *The Menopause Manifesto: Own Your Health With Facts and Feminism*,[36] Dr. Jen Gunter tells us that the loss of menstruation with age is noted in both ancient Chinese and Greek medical writings. Greek and Roman physicians were also very accurate with their recordings of the average age of menopause. Similarly, in 1680, life expectancy for a woman at age 15 (in other words, having survived childhood) in England and Wales was 56.6 years, rising to 64.6 years by 1780.[37] Clearly, life expectancy differed depending on location, relative wealth, health, race, and so on, but at least in the British Isles, many women were living longer a lot earlier than some commentators suggest.

Today women continue to have varied experiences of menopause and associated issues, depending on location, mindset, overall fitness, race, access to health care, and diet. What appears normal for some women is completely abnormal for others. Naturopath Angela Counsel, another great guest on my podcast, questions the accepted normality of *any* symptoms of menopause. She says: "Menopause symptoms are common not normal. If they were normal, we would all experience them. We do not."[38]

When beset by menopause issues, many women will want to take HRT, yet I feel, for most of us, this is like sticking a Band-Aid on a cut. It masks the cut and doesn't allow it to heal. What the cut really needs is to be open to the air. If you're experiencing menopause symptoms, stay curious about what else may be going on. Like Tania Elfersy, I consider menopause symptoms to be the canary in the coal mine. They warn us that all may not be right in our world. We'd do well to listen and address underlying issues rather than mask them and hope for the best. If you suffer badly, HRT can make a big difference and get you back to functioning. From there you can start making diet and lifestyle changes too. Each of us is different. I'm keen to promote the view that there are multiple solutions and not just hormone therapy.

Tania also writes:

"There are still women who swear by HRT or bioidentical HRT and sometimes desensitizing midlife (by changing the hormonal conditions) can be a lifeline when a woman's symptoms appear so devastating. But desensitizing women should not be considered a long-term strategy for well-being, when one considers an individual or the species! Sometimes, we just need to accept that by journeying through our most sensitive times, we will learn something new. It appears part of the design: at midlife we are supposed to wise-up and learn how good health and happiness are created and maintained. This will serve us and those around us for decades to come. Slowly but surely, and despite the backing of a multi-billion-dollar hormone industry, the estrogen theory is crumbling. Every woman who wakes up to her innate wisdom and discovers the true purpose of midlife change helps it crumble some more."[39]

I believe this fundamental wisdom.

I also believe that, unfortunately for some of us, midlife and menopause are times when the way we spent our younger years can catch up with us. I've told you how I believe stress and even possibly air pollution were responsible for my early menopause. If we've lived our lives burning the candle at both ends and not looking after ourselves very well, menopause may be tough. In her book *The New Hot*,[40] Meg Matthews writes about learning she was in menopause in an AA meeting. She experienced all 34 symptoms on the long, scary menopause symptoms list, which you'll find in the Appendix. She's honest about not having lived a particularly healthy life before menopause.

I believe menopause is not necessarily to blame for how bad we may be feeling in midlife. If we choose to listen, it can teach us many lessons. Then it can become that gift I talked about earlier, prompting you to make positive changes that will stand you in good stead long-term.

WHAT YOU MAY EXPERIENCE

You may experience menopause-related issues for a few months, several years, or no time at all. Here are the main ones to look out for. These may appear much earlier than 51 (the average age of menopause) because, as we've discussed, they're really issues associated with perimenopause, which can start any time and is most likely to begin during your mid- to late 40s.

Many women sail through without noticing anything more than the end of their periods. For others, issues often attributed to menopause can include the following:

- Hot flashes (flushes in the UK)
- Night sweats
- Irregular periods
- Trouble sleeping
- Headaches
- Aching joints and muscles
- Restless legs
- Breast tenderness
- Weight gain
- Urinary incontinence
- Changes in skin and hair
- Irritability and forgetfulness
- Anxiety and feelings of insecurity
- Diminished sex drive
- Vaginal dryness

These are the main issues.

What can you do to manage the transition naturally if you don't want to reach for a drug to manage it? Ultimately, however natural and safe HRT may be, it's still a prescription. It's still manufactured from its natural source. It comes in a sachet, patch, or pill format, which means its natural element is highly processed. It's in packaging too, which isn't particularly recyclable if you care about the environment.

HRT AND ME

As I've said, I have discovered many diet and lifestyle changes that can allow us to have a better experience of menopause. Some people believe menopause to be a medical condition, an estrogen deficiency that needs fixing. In line with the book *Feminine Forever*, some believe HRT is the answer to everything menopause related and even long-term women's health. I'm not anti-HRT, far from it. I was advised to take HRT after the early menopause at least until the average menopause age of 51. This was to protect my bones and heart from fewer years of estrogen. Discovering I had borderline osteopenia in my hip after a bone scan finally persuaded me to take HRT.

A word here on terminology again. When I read *The Menopause Manifesto* by Dr. Jen Gunter, I realized there is a new, and I believe better, term for HRT, menopausal hormone therapy or MHT. Dr Gunter writes:

"MHT was called hormone replacement therapy or HRT for years, but that name falsely implies that estrogen or other hormones are missing because of a medical problem, and the low levels of estrogen after menopause are biologically abnormal. Some may argue that the increased risk of cardio-vascular disease after menopause suggests it's a disease, but they're going to lose that argument. As discussed previously if you follow that logic to its conclusion, then being a man is a disease. The messaging matters."

She continues: "It's fair to use the term 'replacement' for women with primary ovarian insufficiency or for those women who have their ovaries surgically removed before natural menopause as estrogen production has stopped pre-maturely, but otherwise MHT should be discussed for what it is—a medical intervention, not a replacement." [41]

Following Dr. Gunter's argument, HRT was the right term for me, having gone through early menopause, but not neces-sarily for older women. I'm going to use the term hormone therapy instead of HRT from now on, as I hope most of my readers will not be going through early menopause like me, and I like Dr Gunter's point of view.

I was given the advice to stay on hormone therapy only until average menopause age if I was feeling okay, and I took this advice to heart. I weaned myself off at 51. I have an inher-ent dislike of taking medication unless I absolutely have to. High blood pressure didn't go away after pregnancy, and I was advised to take medication because of family history. I took my BP meds at first, but subsequently tried lifestyle changes to keep my BP normal. I take a similar approach to menopause. I don't want to medicalize a natural transition in a woman's life unless absolutely necessary. We don't auto-matically medicate puberty, and I don't believe hormone therapy should be the default option when it comes to menopause.

When I try to communicate this preference and my rationale behind it, I often get into trouble. I'm accused of judging women who choose to take hormone therapy. Let me be clear, it's a woman's right to choose whether she takes hormone therapy or not. There are some women for whom medical advice is most certainly that they should take hormone therapy; for example, if menopause comes early or has been brought on by illness or surgery or there are other complications. But many of us won't need it. I want you to have all the information you need to be able to make informed decisions about hormone therapy and other solutions. I'd prefer if most women only took hormone therapy to get them through the difficult times, not that it becomes a long-term panacea for all issues related to natural aging in women, as some menopause practitioners are now suggesting.

In her book *The XX Brain, The Groundbreaking Science Empowering Women to Prevent Dementia*, Dr. Laura Mosconi writes:

"Let me underline that the primary indication for MHT remains relief of hot flashes, night sweats, and vaginal dryness. MHT is not recommended for prevention of heart disease, Alzheimer's, cognitive decline, or any other conditions."[42]

She goes on to say:

"I must reiterate that prescription medicines come with many potentially dangerous side effects of their own, and the last thing any of us needs is to accidentally exchange one negative side effect for another. Another reason to look beyond estrogen replacement is the fact that estrogen is not always a friendly and helpful substance—especially when it's not your own. It doesn't cost much to start with the safer strategies that focus on ameliorating hormonal levels by means of diet, exercise, and other natural therapies. These methods are known to boost hormonal production in the brain as well as in the body, while improving memory, sharpening our minds, and supporting resilience, all the while reducing risk of dementia for all women, no matter what stage of the game they're at."[43]

Women in the Blue Zones[44], where people live the longest, don't rely on HRT for their long healthspan. We are all guinea pigs when it comes to long-term use of HRT. There is some new research on the safest window for taking HRT and in *The Menopause Manifesto*, Dr. Gunter writes:

"The North American Menopause Society (NAMS) guidelines, which have been endorsed by almost every major American and international medical society dedicated to women's health, state that for women under the age of sixty or who are within ten years of menopause and have no contraindications, MHT is an appropriate choice for treating vasomotor symptoms (hot flushes and night sweats), preventing osteoporosis, and treatment of genitourinary syndrome of menopause (GUSM).[45]

Personally, I'd rather stay on the side of caution when it comes to long-term use of hormone therapy. In her book, *The New Hot*, Meg Matthews includes the menopause experience of Buck Angel, a transgender man. He writes about how taking testosterone for 10 years atrophied his reproductive system...

"...causing my uterus to fuse with my cervix, creating an infection in my uterus. That was the cramping I had been experiencing all these years... After three months on intensive antibiotics to get rid of the infection, I then had a full laparoscopic vaginal hysterectomy... All of this could have been prevented if any one of my endocrinologists would have given me an estrogen supplement... How can doctors be giving a very powerful hormone like testosterone without understanding the need to balance this out... I almost died because of the lack of medical knowledge, yet the doctors give testosterone out with little concern about the long-term effects."[46]

I'm not suggesting that long-term use of systemic hormone therapy for women could cause similar issues. Of course not. I am suggesting there's still not enough knowledge about the long-term effects of any hormone therapy for some practitioners to be so confident telling women it's okay to be on it long term or even forever, as Robert A. Wilson tried to do in 1966.

I see hormone therapy as a temporary solution, not a permanent one. If it's right for you, go for it. I think it can be particularly useful for women under high levels of stress that cannot quickly and easily be reduced – though that does need to be a long-term goal. Hormone therapy is positioned as the cure-all for the whole range of menopause symptoms because it restores the hormonal profile you had before perimenopause started. It mutes symptoms that may actually be the body shouting for us to take notice and make changes. We're designed to live the latter part of our lives with less estrogen. That's what we do. It's not a deficiency, nor does it diminish us. We have evolved that way.

Whether you choose hormone therapy or not, read this section to get a broad perspective on how to balance your hormones long term. What I suggest should help regardless of whether you're on hormone therapy or not. I chose to come off systemic hormone therapy at 51 and have since managed any issues mostly naturally. I'm glad to report that my bone density has remained stable. I occasionally take localized vaginal estrogen to help with dryness; more on that later. For me, it makes sense to find other ways to get our hormones in balance long term whenever possible.

FINDING YOUR BALANCE: HOW TO EASE THE PHYSICAL, MENTAL AND EMOTIONAL CHANGES

Let's start with how to achieve better overall hormonal balance naturally, and in the following chapters, I'll give ideas on what you can do for specific issues.

1. Balance your blood sugar

Start with what and how you eat. As Jackie Lynch writes in her book *The Happy Menopause*,[47] the most fundamental component of good hormonal balance in midlife and beyond is making sure your blood sugar levels are as stable as possible. This viewpoint reflects the advice I was given all those years ago. As we go through the perimenopause years, estrogen decreases, but it doesn't go away completely. The ovaries stop producing it, but a weaker form is still found in our adipose tissue and produced by our adrenal glands. Even the brain makes its own estrogen.[48] The problem is that if we're stressed and our bodies go into fight or flight mode, the adrenal glands prioritize production of our stress hormones in favor of estrogen. Then we can get into trouble with menopause issues.

Stress can be emotional, or it can be stress we put on our bodies because our blood sugar levels are imbalanced. This happens either because we haven't eaten when we should have, and blood sugar has dropped, or we've consumed the wrong thing that makes our blood sugar level spike. Eating and drinking the right things, and doing it regularly, becomes ever more important. Caffeine, alcohol, sugar, and refined foods can all cause our blood sugar to spike and then plummet when their effects wear off. Eating a little and often, as well as eating protein and complex carbohydrates high in fiber (such as beans, whole grains, and starchy vegetables) with every meal, is a good way to go. Now's the perfect time to make your diet healthier overall and include lots of fresh vegetables. Cut out processed food as much as you can. Refined carbohydrates, in particular, are known to mess with our hormones generally, quite apart from the blood sugar-spiking effect.[49]

2. Add plant phytoestrogens to your healthy diet

It's also a great idea to increase your consumption of natural phytoestrogens, which are thought to help replace the estrogen lost by the body during perimenopause. Women from cultures that eat foodstuffs like soy, with a higher level of natural phytoestrogens, such as Japan and China, often appear to experience fewer menopause symptoms. A recent study published by the North American Menopause Society found that a plant-based diet rich in soy reduces moderate to severe hot flashes by 84% from nearly five per day to fewer than one per day. Overall hot flashes (including mild ones) decreased by 79%.[50] Isn't that cool! I gave up dairy milk over a decade ago and replaced it with organic soy. I still eat cheese and other dairy products but not as much as before. (Many of us get more intolerant to dairy products as we age, and I'm wary of hormones in cow's milk.) I also consume soy products, such as tofu and miso, and I try to keep these as unrefined as possible. Highly refined soy products, like tofu nuggets, for example, are not good for you. Traditional and/ or fermented soy products usually are.[51]

It's also possible to balance hormones better with simple foods like seeds. For instance, I have two teaspoons of ground flax seeds on my muesli or in some organic soy milk each morning. I also have sunflower seeds, pumpkin seeds, chia seeds, and hemp seeds. I call this my "hormonal balance breakfast." (See the box at the end of this chapter for the recipe.) Soaked flaxseeds are also effective; soak overnight, then drink them and the water the next day. I just prefer mine ground. I'm also addicted to hummus. All of these foods are good sources of natural phytoestrogens, and I'm convinced they've helped me transition more easily through menopause and get off hormone therapy. I recently found out sprouted greens such as cress, mustard, alfalfa, and broccoli sprouts are also good sources of plant hormones. According to the book *Grow Your Own HRT*,[52] you can even grow your own red clover, which is the key ingredient in many menopause supplements. Sprouted mung beans as well as bean sprouts and sesame seeds are also good sources of phytoestrogens and, interestingly, are also important in the Chinese diet.

3. Avoid toxins in food and elsewhere

It can be expensive, but eat organic if you can for all food types. Pesticides used in agriculture are known to impact our hormones negatively and are generally not very good for you. The increase in these and other products, such as hormones and antibiotics in the food chain, as well as chemicals in our personal care products (see below), could be a key factor explaining why Western women suffer more from menopause now than in the past and more than women in other parts of the world. Certain fruits and vegetables have more pesticide residues on them than others. You don't need to worry about everything, but some foodstuffs are particularly prone to toxicity. I'm still grappling with all this but have printed out the lists of the worst offenders and other foods you can worry less about for reference. You can get these lists, the Dirty Dozen and the Clean Fifteen for the UK, at Pesticide Action Network,[53] or in the US at the EWG[54] (Environmental Working Group).

Consider also which toxins are in your home environment and whether you can cut back on those. Household cleaning products are full of chemicals, some of which are thought to interfere with hormones. Personal products like deodorant, moisturizers, shampoos, and so on often come laden with potentially suspect ingredients (there's still controversy about parabens, for example.[55]) Can you identify everything in the ingredient list of your favorite product? European regulations on what's allowed in personal products are more stringent than those in the US, but we simply don't know the long-term effects from daily use of many ingredients that are allowed.

EWG research found that American women use an average of 12 products a day on their bodies, containing 168 different chemicals.[56] I've followed advice to try to cut back on these, both for my own health and for the environment. It's about reducing the cumulative toxic load that you are putting your body under. I now use less toxic cleaning and laundry products when I can and try to keep personal care products as natural as possible. That's not to say I don't sometimes indulge in some less natural "beauty boosting" skincare, but I'm always conscious of what that might contribute to my overall toxic load. There are many alternatives to conventional skincare, for example. For me, this means organic coconut oil to clean my face and take off makeup or even just water with one of those fluffy makeup-removing cloths. You could create a simple organic facial oil blend and whipped organic shea butter or argan oil to moisturize, depending on the season, what needs moisturizing, and how dry your skin is.

4. Reduce emotional stress

Try to reduce your emotional stress or improve how you deal with it. As we've seen, hormone fluctuations are exacerbated by stress, whether it's real, imagined, or diet-related. (Remember my early menopause?) Maybe embrace a simpler life, adopt a meditation or journaling practice, or do some restorative yoga. All these will help you lower stress levels overall and potentially reduce menopause symptoms, especially the anxiety that seems to affect many of us around this time. Getting this right in the menopause years will set you up for long-term health. In her book, *The XX Brain*, Dr. Lisa Mosconi talks about the huge impact of stress on hormones, aging, and menopause.

"Especially for women, research shows that prolonged periods of stress, and the subsequent surge in cortisol levels, decreases overall cell function while sending our hormonal levels plummeting, which can accelerate neuronal aging and aggravate the symptoms of menopause."[57]

Don't forget the power of your mind! How you approach menopause can impact your experience of it, as with aging in general. Stay curious about what's happening to you and be open to the possibilities menopause and aging can bring. Lots more on that to come.

5. Manage your weight

Get a handle on your weight if you think it's an issue. We talk in more detail about maintaining a healthy weight later on, but if you're significantly overweight in midlife, that will cause problems now and down the line. Overweight women are known to have more of an issue with hot flashes, in particular.[58] Excess weight isn't going to help with aches and pains either. Yes, you can take a supplement or try other things here that will help. But if you are overweight and suffering badly with menopause symptoms, consider trying to do something about it rather than just accepting it as a natural aspect of getting older. It's not.

6. Prioritize exercise

Make a point of prioritizing exercise. As we age, we need more exercise, not less, to take care of our bodies, and many women swear by exercise to help them manage menopause symptoms as well as general stress.[59] I know that regular yoga, running, and strength training certainly help me. I think every human being should do yoga! It's just so very good for our bodies if done properly. What's a good exercise regimen for menopause? Yoga or Pilates to stretch out the body, help with achy joints, and manage stress; some sort of cardio that gets your heart rate up (e.g., speed walking, dancing, running, rowing, or Zumba class) to protect your heart, help manage stress, and minimize weight gain; some form of weight-bearing exercise (e.g., running or jumping) to maintain bone density; and lifting weights to maintain muscle mass and physical strength, and also help keep your metabolism up.

7. Try acupuncture

If you're open to trying it, acupuncture is known to be helpful for issues with hormonal balance throughout a woman's life.[60] It can also help with fertility issues. My friend had a baby naturally after being told she'd gone through early menopause. She credits acupuncture for the birth, and subsequently retrained as an acupuncturist. It may be worth a try, especially if you feel you need an extra boost.

Before we get into the details of how to manage specific menopause issues, such as hot flashes, brain fog, hair problems, restless legs, and so on, I thought I'd share some good stuff about life after menopause—because there is a lot of good stuff!

THINGS TO LOOK FORWARD TO POST MENOPAUSE

I asked women in my free Facebook group, "The Flock,"[61] what they liked most about being postmenopausal, and this is what they had to say.

- "I feel a sense of freedom around my body and my life. Can't really explain it, but having left behind all those reproductive issues, as well as many other things, I'm in total control now."
- "I like that I feel freer—like going back prepuberty, in a way. I love that I feel able to focus on what I want rather than being so focused on everybody else's needs now that my estrogen is no longer running the show."
- "My moods are much more stable now [that] I'm no longer on an estrogen roller coaster."
- "I know that everything I do, think, feel is me, not a mad rush of hormones that take over my body and mind. I can feel the effect of vitamins and supplements straight away and am in tune with the effect

food and drink have on my body and mind. When I reflect, I would say it's a good, calm feeling!"

- "Firstly, I no longer have the horrible pain I had with Endometriosis (yay!) Secondly, I finally let go of any lingering hope of having children (it wasn't until I did it that I realized how badly I had needed to do that). Thirdly, as others have said, my moods are much more stable. I feel more in control of them now (and, there-fore, of my life). Love it!"
- "I've lost the cravings for chocolate! I'm less tolerant and more likely to speak up now."
- "I have more energy and focus and a general sense of well-being."
- "Feeling at peace with myself and a deep understand-ing of myself, which the menopausal process gifted me."

MY HORMONAL BALANCE BREAKFAST

Most mornings I have what I call my "hormonal balance breakfast." This consists of some sugar-free muesli, mainly oats, with organic soy milk. I add 2 teaspoons of ground golden flaxseeds, 1-2 teaspoons of pumpkin and sunflower seeds, a few hemp seeds, some chia seeds, 5-8 goji berries, a small teaspoon of maca powder and 1/2 teaspoon of ashwaganda powder, plus any berries, such as blueberries or raspberries, I have in stock. This gives me a good boost of natural phytoestrogens first thing in the morning, as well as other great nutrients to kick-start my day. I have absolutely no need for caffeine, having not had any for over a decade. I'm very partial to Clipper organic decaffeinated "builders" tea (in the UK this is what we call strong black tea) with my organic soy milk. Yum!

CHECK-IN

Write down the answers to these questions in your notebook or journal.

- What have you learned about balancing hormones that you didn't know before?
- How do you feel about managing your menopause naturally?
- What are three things you could start doing straight away that may make a difference to how you feel?
- How can you start managing your stress better if this is an issue for you?
- What is one household product you could swap this week for something more natural?
- How good is your physical fitness? What could you do to improve it?

CHAPTER SIX

GETTING DOWN TO SPECIFIC MENOPAUSE ISSUES: HOT FLASHES, ETC.

"The best advice on aging is this: what's the alternative? The alternative, of course, is death. And that's a lot of shit to deal with. So I'm happy to deal with menopause. I'll take it."
Whoopi Goldberg

This is where we get into detail on some of the most common issues that might be troubling you around menopause. Hot flashes, brain fog, anxiety, weight gain—watch out! We're coming for you! If you're looking for help with libido, vaginal dryness, or incontinence, jump ahead to Chapter Seven.

HOT FLASHES AND NIGHT SWEATS

The most common menopause symptom is hot flashes and their nighttime equivalent, night sweats. There's often a sense of shame associated with these, as well as lots of frustration. There's no need to feel embarrassed or apologetic. Do men apologize because they lose their hair? Of course not!

Here's how you can cool down these two symptoms:

1.   First, think of them as power surges, and they instantly become less of an issue. They're great when it's chilly! This may sound simplistic and naïve, especially if you're coping with being drenched in sweat, but it's worth a go. Mind over matter, perhaps? A BBC documentary on menopause showed that when women used Cognitive Behavioral Therapy (CBT) techniques to change their beliefs about hot flashes (mainly shame, which led to stress), their flashes became fewer and less intense.[62]

2.   Keep a diary of when you have hot flashes and the triggers for them. Is stress bringing them on? Caffeine? Sugar? Alcohol? Chili? All these are known to exacerbate hot flashes. If you know the triggers, you can tackle the symptoms. Keep an eye on your weight, too, as being overweight won't help.

3.   Find ways to reduce stress if this triggers a hot flash. I found that when I was under pressure, that was exactly when my body started to heat up. If you're in a meeting and a hot flash happens, don't be embarrassed to step outside until it subsides. Or, have a big glass of cold water on hand. It takes courage to be honest about what's going on, but a little humor and honesty might be just the ticket and could also help others. If honesty isn't possible, make an excuse and leave for "some air."

4.   Try avoiding or reducing caffeine. For many women, caffeine brings on a hot flash. I haven't had any caffeine since I went through early menopause at 41. I was advised to give it up, and I haven't missed it in years. I love not being dependent on it to get myself going in

the morning or after lunch. I love a good decaf English tea, though.

5. Cut back on sugar, especially refined. Refined-sugar products are known to cause hot flashes. I try not to overdo it on the sugar front, but I do love my chocolate, which I try to keep mostly dark. The mini hot flash I occasionally get after I've had some chocolate is worth it. It's just my little power surge!

6. If you find alcohol a trigger, consider reducing that too. Sadly, it's many of the things we enjoy that contribute to our power surges. I'm not saying you should cut alcohol out completely, but it's better to be informed so you can make decisions that work for you. Again, remember your body may be telling you that what you've done in the past may not be what you need for long-term future health. I know women who continue to drink quite heavily while taking hormone therapy to stop their flashes. That's probably not doing them a lot of good long-term.

7. Learn to regulate your temperature with ease. Wear scarves and layers that can be opened or removed. I gave up wearing turtlenecks because I don't want to run the risk of being caught having a hot flash and unable to do anything about it. Avoid synthetic fabrics and carry a pocket foldout fan, especially in summer. I'm also usually found with a hair band on my wrist. I have long hair, and my hair band helps regulate my temperature. Drink plenty of water.

8. If night sweats are the biggest issue, make sure you're wearing and sleeping in natural fabrics. Ensure the room

is well-ventilated, and consider sleeping separately for a while if your partner likes it warmer than you do. Avoid alcohol, as this can really cause nighttime sweats.

9. Finally, consider these natural remedies, too[63]:

Black cohosh
Maca powder (in smoothies)
Spirulina (in smoothies)
Sage (as a supplement or just as a tea)
Chamomile tea
Dong Quai, a Chinese herb

ANXIETY AND DEPRESSION

Anxiety can often raise its nervous head during the menopause transition. If you think of premenstrual syndrome (PMS), it's only natural that as hormones fluctuate more in perimenopause, our nerves may be more on edge. Women can become depressed around this time and are often offered antidepressants by their doctor, when what they really need is help balancing their hormones.

But don't automatically blame menopause! There's potentially a ton of other causes that may be making you more anxious and sad than usual. You may be suffering the effects of ageism and sexism and all those negative narratives about who you are now, not to mention the global pandemic we've been coping with as I write this, and the U-curve of happiness. Antidepressants may help you through a difficult patch, but often it's more about balancing our hormones and dealing with some of the emotional issues that surface around this time. Like hormone therapy, antidepressants can enable us to function, but they may mask symptoms we need to deal with, whether or not we take medication. Obviously, for some women, antidepressants are essential, but jumping straight to prescribing them for a midlife woman is not really giving her the duty of care required, in my opinion.

Statistics on menopause and mental health can also appear alarming. For example, there's an unfortunate correlation which keeps being raised in the UK media, between menopause and the age at which there is the highest rate of suicide for women. It's true that women aged 50-54 exhibit the highest rate of suicide in the UK,[64] but the actual rate is only 7.4 women per 100,000 population. This rate compares with 6.9 women per 100,000 in the 45-49 age range and 6.5 in the 55-59 age range. Of course, any rate of suicide is awful. But this is a tiny increase between age ranges, and the rate of male suicide is greater than that of women in every age group except 15-19. I think conflating the age at which there is the highest rate of female suicide with menopause is irresponsible, especially without context, and plays on women's fears about this time. It appears that even science can skew statistics against mature women!

I believe there are many other factors that build up for women in midlife that also impact our mental well-being. Sometimes I feel like the great menopause defender: "It's not her fault!" If you're experiencing anxiety and low mood, I encourage you to be curious about what's going on underneath and how you can deal with it.

There are plenty of things that can help, whatever the root cause. Here are some:

1. Try any or all of the general hormonal balance tips in Chapter Five.

2. Remember, if you're a drinker, alcohol is a depressant, and your body may not be able to cope with it as well as it once did.

3. Try a regular meditation practice and mindfulness too. This will help ground you and bring you back to living in the moment. Good mindfulness/meditation apps to try are Calm, Headspace, Buddify, and Insight Timer (which is free).

4. Exercise and being outdoors are great for anxiety and depression. Go for a walk in the park (or in a forest, if you can find one) and take some deep, calming breaths.

5. Take big belly breaths. Many of us breathe very shallowly, in our upper chest. This doesn't help at all when you're feeling anxious. Slow things down and breathe deep into your belly. Do it 10 times and assess whether you feel less anxious. Box breathing[65] is another technique to try. With box breathing, you breathe in for four seconds, hold for four seconds, breathe out for four seconds, and hold for four seconds, all while visualizing moving round the sides of a square.

6. EFT (Emotional Freedom Technique), otherwise known as tapping meditation, can also be very helpful for anxiety. It has been found to be particularly effective for veterans suffering from PTSD.[66] I really like The Tapping Solution app.[67]

7. I recently discovered essential oils and am finding them very powerful for changing my mood. I've been experimenting with blends in a diffuser to help me focus, boost my energy, balance emotions, and calm me down. You can find lots of blend ideas to try on lovingessentialoils. com.[68]

8. Remember that menopause doesn't make you any less of who you are. You are still the fabulous woman you've always been. You know the same stuff and can do the same things. Believe in yourself and your power.

9. If anxiety and low mood tip over into depression, be sure to visit your doctor and get whatever help you need. The longer you leave it, the worse it may get.

IRREGULAR AND HEAVY BLEEDING

Most women will experience irregular bleeding, and for some women periods can get very heavy, even leading to flooding. Keeping track of your cycles can be really informative, so keep a diary to give you more of an idea of what's going on with your body. You may experience less or more frequent periods and lighter or heavier ones. We all have a different experience. Just when you think you may be through menopause at last, your ovaries can have other plans and you'll have a bleed. If your periods are a lot heavier, longer, or more frequent, get yourself checked out by your doctor. If you bleed after a year or two without a period, definitely get yourself checked out by a doctor. *The Menopause Manifesto*[69] has a whole chapter on this which I highly recommend reading if periods are an issue for you.

SLEEP ISSUES

Sleep can be an issue in the menopause years, but it should get better once hormonal fluctuations stop. It's not just the quantity of sleep we get that matters. It's also the quality of our sleep. Sleeplessness can affect many women during menopause, but if it continues afterwards, then you need to seek help because it's become a habit. There are many things we can do to try to get more and better sleep. Sleep is so important, especially as we age.

Start by trying everything in Chapter Five to get your hormones in balance. Cut back on caffeine, sugar, and alcohol, because these are not going to help your hormonal balance or your sleep. If restless legs (see below) are keeping you awake, try a magnesium supplement and leg stretches before bed. Practice good sleep hygiene: make it dark and quiet where you sleep, stop using screens an hour before bed, and create a soothing routine to get you ready for sleep (think bath time for babies. We need routine too).

If you're lying awake thinking, choose to not think. Tell yourself, "Now is not the time for thinking, now is the time for sleeping." Try meditating as you lie there. You may just drift off. Arianna Huffington swears by this approach and sees sleeplessness as an opportunity to meditate. She's written a whole book about the importance of sleep in which she shares many of these techniques, *The Sleep Revolution*.[70]

EFT can also help with insomnia, as recommended by a member of my community who went through surgical menopause with no hormone therapy, using the Tapping Solution app.[71] Even if results are partly due to the placebo effect, if you find that tapping works for you, so what? You'll still have a better night's sleep.

BRAIN FOG

Brain fog is an issue for many women, often made worse by fear. When we find ourselves forgetting things or getting a bit muddled and we don't know why, our first thought can be that it's early onset Alzheimer's. There is such fear of dementia, particularly in the West, that many women fear this is what's happening to them when they can't remember the word they need. That's another reason to raise awareness about this common menopause issue. I wonder if you've had this experience? If so, fear not!

When our hormones start fluctuating, they affect many things, including our ability to think as clearly as before. Hopefully, post menopause, this will settle down, but during the perimenopause years, we need to sort our hormonal balance as much as we can and develop coping strategies for when we suffer some brain fog. Go back to Chapter Five on how to get better overall hormonal balance. That will give your brain and body the best chance of thriving through menopause.

You probably don't need me to tell you that if you're suffering from insomnia due to hormonal fluctuations, you're also likely to suffer from foggy brain. Make sure you're getting enough good, deep sleep. If it's still an issue, consider coping strategies like a bit of humor to take away the anxiety. Try not to take it too seriously; we all forget things. For most of us, forgetfulness won't indicate a deeper issue, but if you're especially worried or have a family history of brain issues, do get yourself checked out. Sleep, stress, nutrition, and exercise will all have an impact on brain fog. *Beating Brain Fog: Your 30-Day Plan to Think Faster, Sharper, Better* by Dr. Sabina Brennan[72] has lots more research-based tips if you're struggling.

I sometimes get a bit muddled still, but I think I've always been a bit like that. If you try not to let it upset you, it will have less impact. If you fear brain fog is impacting your performance at work, consider talking about it with a manager if that's possible. If you have a good relationship with colleagues, perhaps you can tell them brain fog is just something that happens. It all helps raise awareness. Ask them to help you with a forgotten word and move swiftly on. Not being able to remember something or feeling a bit muddled doesn't make you any less of the highly capable woman you've always been.

RESTLESS LEGS

I think restless legs is one of the strangest conditions associated with menopause. I've experienced it myself, particularly when I've been rushing about and my own personal self-care has slipped down the priority list. The exact cause remains unknown, but there are various things that can cause or trigger restless legs, such as an iron deficiency, being overweight, or having too much caffeine. Personally, I find if I'm not drinking alcohol and I'm doing enough yoga, I'm less likely to be kept awake by my restless legs. If I've been running a lot and not stretching enough, I'm in trouble. One thing that really helps is taking a magnesium supplement. Magnesium deficiency can cause problems with nerve impulse conduction and muscle contractions and can cause muscle cramps.[73] Stretching your legs before bed can also help.

ACHY JOINTS

Menopause gets blamed for many things, including achy joints. This condition could easily be caused by other issues. Ultimately, it may just be due to getting older, but it's far more likely to be caused in midlife by insufficient care of your body. Hormonal fluctuations aren't going to help. Aches and pains are your body trying to talk to you. What is aching, and what can you do to make that better? Yoga, Pilates, or any kind of regular stretching will help to keep you both flexible and pain free. Staying mobile is also key. We often ache because we don't move about enough, especially if we're very sedentary. Don't let aches and pains stop you from moving. If you're overweight, you may also find that your joints ache more as your estrogen levels drop.

Dehydration is never good for us and can also impact joint pain and stiffness. Keep up your fluids, especially if you experience night sweats. Stress can also impact joint health, so while you're stretching, think about meditation and general mindfulness to try to relieve stress. Think about your nutrition too. An anti-inflammatory diet[74] will help with pain, and it's thought by some that removing nightshade vegetables from your diet can help with arthritis and inflammation, for example.[75]

HAIR ISSUES

Hormonal changes can impact our hair as well. We often start finding it in places we don't want it—our chins, and don't find as much of it in the places we want it—our heads. Hair loss can be caused by multiple factors, but aging and hormonal changes can definitely take their share of the blame, as can stress, again. Getting better hormonal balance overall will help.

Let's start with hair loss, which can be particularly distressing. If there's no obvious medical reason for your hair loss, and it's bad, please be sure to get it checked out. Otherwise, there are various approaches that may help with thinning hair. First, it helps to go as natural as possible with your hair products. As I've said, these days we can't be sure what's in any personal product and the impact it may have long term. It pays to try to move more towards the natural/organic end of the range. Hair products that contain phthalates or parabens can increase damage to your hair and scalp, so check your ingredients. In addition, we can get more sensitive to these ingredients as we go through menopause. If you can't identify the ingredients, buy another product.

Hair coloring is usually made of chemicals that damage the scalp and hair unless you're using all natural products. The same goes with bleaching or perming. If you can avoid these chemicals, give that a try to see if it helps rejuvenate your hair. Lots of blow drying, curling, or straightening is also not going to help build lustrous locks. Avoid shampooing every day, as it washes out the natural oils in your hair. If you have very dry hair, it might be worth applying coconut or argan oil to bring back lost natural oils. There will be hair thickening products and supplements available in your local pharmacy, although these may not be especially natural—proceed with caution!

If all else fails, don't be afraid to consider a wig. I once spent a very pleasant afternoon at a wig shop with a friend of mine. She has a healthy head of her own hair, but like many Black women, enjoys experimenting with different hair styles by using wigs. Watching her try all the different ones and admiring her immediate transformation was really enlightening for me. I think many women feel wearing a wig is something shameful. Many of us could learn a lot from following the example of our Black sisters and experiment a bit. A wig is also better for you than extensions, which can cause untold damage to the health of your own hair.

A quick note on hormone therapy and hair. One of my mentoring clients wanted to come off hormone therapy because she felt it caused her hair to fall out. When she weaned herself off, her hair grew back. Another client wanted to go on hormone therapy because she felt menopause caused her hair to fall out, and she noticed an improvement after starting hormone therapy. So don't make assumptions about what may be causing hair issues. Stay curious.

Then, of course, there's the issue of finding hair where we don't want it. Why is hair determined to move from our head to our chin? Certainly, invest in a magnifying mirror, as the combination of chin hair and farsightedness is not a good one (unless it just doesn't bother you). I have one particularly irritating hair on my chin. I have very few white hairs on my head, but this chin one is brilliant white. If I leave it for too long, it becomes a veritable whisker! I pluck it when I remember. If unwanted hair is upsetting for you, there are options, such as laser treatment or bleaching. Again, my instinct is to stay as natural as possible, even (and especially) when it comes to facial hair.

WEIGHT GAIN

Earlier, I touched on the importance of maintaining a healthy weight for hormonal balance. Here are some more tips on how to minimize midlife weight gain.

1. Don't assume weight gain is inevitable

We often assume weight gain is inevitable as we age, and especially in menopause. Those pesky fluctuating hormones don't help, but it's also age and decreasing muscle at fault. During and after menopause, we tend to store our fat around the middle more. Stress increases this tendency. We can store more fat around our middle for years without actually realizing it or dealing with our stress. We already know menopause issues are exacerbated by stress. Estrogen is also found in our adipose tissue, so the menopausal body may be reluctant to let go of fat stores. Midlife, menopause, and the stress that goes alongside them can create the perfect storm in which it becomes harder to maintain a healthy weight. But it's not impossible!

2. Be wary of fat in the middle

A few extra pounds may not really matter, but there are two things to consider here. First, are you comfortable carrying those extra pounds? If you are, that's probably fine. But if they're accumulating around your middle, which is where they do for most of us, it's not good for your health. That's when we're best advised to instigate a long-term weight maintenance plan (otherwise known as a change in lifestyle) so weight gain doesn't become a pattern. In her book *Fat Around the Middle*, Dr. Marilyn Glenville writes:

"Scientists now know that storing fat in the middle of your body rather than anywhere else has major health implications and studies show that it increases the risk of heart disease, diabetes, stroke, cancer and high blood pressure." [76]

3. Calculate your healthy weight

For our personal sense of well-being and our long-term health, it pays to maintain a healthy weight. But what is a healthy weight? There are three things to consider. A commonly accepted measure of whether or not you're overweight is the body mass index (BMI).[77] This is the ratio of your height to your weight. But be aware: there are drawbacks to the BMI, as it cannot allow for variations in fat, bone, organs, or muscle. Muscle can weigh three times as much as fat, and it's extremely important to consider where your fat is situated, as we've seen.

How do you measure your body fat, assuming it's pretty clear where it is? There are machines available, often in gyms or to buy, that you can use to measure what proportion of your body is made up of fat. These were completely new to me, and I have to confess I've never even seen one! But if you fancy actually measuring your fat, using one of these machines will give you a percentage score that will fit in the following categories for women.[78]

Age	Healthy percentage
20-39	21-32%
40-59	23-33%
60-79	24-35%

Maybe they think no one will bother with what proportion of their body is fat by age 80? Ageist!

The easiest and potentially most important figure to use in determining your future health is a very simple measurement, the difference between your hips and your waist. Dr. Glenville says:

"This is the true measure of fat around the middle and the best indicator of whether or not you are going to be vulnerable to all the health risks associated with it. Take a tape measure and compare your waist measurement at the narrowest point with your hip measurement at the widest point, and divide the waist figure by the hip figure to get what is known as your waist to hip ratio. A figure greater than 0.8 means that you are apple shaped and would benefit from getting rid of some of that fat."[79]

4. Maintain your metabolism

Some of our midlife weight gain is due to not maintaining muscle mass. Muscle burns calories faster than fat, and from the age of around 30, our muscle mass starts to naturally decline. If we're not doing exercise, particularly weight-bearing exercise, to maintain our muscle mass, we have no way of slowing down its deterioration. Our metabolism may slow down as the proportion of muscle in our bodies relative to fat declines. I hear women say they don't understand it when they eat the same as they ate before and do the same amount of exercise, and they still put on weight. It used to be thought that this was because our metabolism naturally slows as we age. However, recent studies have found that our metabolism doesn't actually start to decline because of age until we hit 60.[80] But, if we are burning less fat because we have less muscle, we will still put on weight if we consume the same as we did when we had more muscle. If we're fit, do regular, sufficient (and the right kind of) exercise, and have strong muscle mass, it's possible we won't experience weight gain in midlife or later on.

5. Maintain a stable blood sugar level—again

Remember earlier, when I talked about the impact of blood sugar levels on hormonal balance? Weight is affected too. As I've said, we tend to store fat when we're under stress. One of the easiest ways our body believes we're under stress is through fluctuating blood sugar levels. So, eating small, regular meals and snacks is a better way to go than having long periods when we don't eat. This approach effectively means eating three not overly substantial meals a day, including some kind of protein and healthy nutritional snacks in between. There are many sources of protein, both animal and plant based. You can get protein from eggs, fish, meat, dairy food, nuts and seeds, and all forms of soy (including soybeans, tofu, or tempeh). Intermittent fasting may not be an easy way to lose weight during menopause because it will cause fluctuating blood sugar levels which may impact the body's stress response.[81]

Foods with a high glycemic index, such as refined carbohydrates, cause an immediate and substantial increase in blood sugar, and also a big drop afterward. Better to eat foods that have a low glycemic index, where energy is released slowly over time without causing a spike in blood sugar levels. Eating this way will help with menopausal symptoms in general.

A modern diet high on the glycemic index is another of the many reasons, I believe, why menopause symptoms in the West appear to have gotten worse as time has gone on. Nowadays, we consume far more processed foods and sugar than our ancestors ever did. Sugar will have the biggest impact on your blood sugar level of any food, and we just don't need it. If you want to lose weight, cut out sugar as much as possible. When you become aware, it seems sugar is absolutely everywhere. So get into the habit of checking labels if you want to avoid it.

6. No starchy carbohydrates after six in the evening

We only really need starchy carbs if we're doing lots of physical activity. If you eat carbs after six in the evening when you're likely at your most inactive, these will turn straight into fat. Avoid rice, potatoes, or pasta, even the brown and whole grain varieties, if you can. It may not be an option all the time, such as when you're eating out, but at least try to follow this rule most of the time.

There's so much good information out there about how we can maintain a healthy weight or lose excess weight, especially when it comes to diet. There isn't room in this book to cover it all, and I'm not a nutritionist, but I hope I've given you a good place to start. I recommend Dr. Glenville's book[82] because she focuses on the issues of midlife women. She says we should aim to eat healthfully at least 80% of the time, allowing ourselves 20% off for good behavior.

CHECK-IN

Write down the answers to these questions in your notebook or journal.

- What are some potential solutions for any menopause-related issues you may be experiencing?
- Are you aware of any correlations between your symptoms and your diet or lifestyle? If not, try keeping a food/lifestyle diary and start tracking symptoms to see what correlations there might be.
- What can you apply now to help you thrive through menopause?
- Are you a healthy weight? What ideas could you apply to get to one or maintain yours?

CHAPTER SEVEN

GETTING DOWN TO SPECIFIC MENOPAUSE ISSUES: SEX, ETC.

"There is no greater power in the world than the zest of a postmenopausal woman."
Margaret Mead

I decided the biggest taboo of menopause deserved a chapter all to itself. Changes in our sexual response can be one of the most upsetting aspects of menopause and certainly one of the least talked about. But it doesn't have to be. Let's get down to business!

LACK OF LIBIDO AND VAGINAL DRYNESS

I've put these two topics together, as I think they're linked. If one isn't working, the other probably won't work either! These two combined can be the most distressing issues for many women who've previously enjoyed an active sex life. While many women don't experience issues, I think a lot of us do, and because we don't talk about it, none of us knows just how many of us have problems. Shame kicks in, and some women give up on sex completely. But it doesn't have to be like that. Don't despair! Help is at hand. This section is mainly for heterosexual couples. There is often more of a pleasure gap between men and women as we age than there is between two women, for example, but many of these principles apply to all couples.

1. Don't assume lack of libido is necessarily caused by menopause

You might just be bored, stressed, completely emotionally depleted, or all of the above! By the time your hormones settle post menopause, you may actually have more testosterone in your body relative to other sex hormones than ever before. You may be raring to go. Other issues, such as vaginal dryness, may complicate matters if your libido is fine. This is one instance of mismatch between dryness and libido. On the other hand, you may have been in your relationship for a very long time by the time you get to midlife, and sex could just be a bit dull. So go easy on yourself and stay open to possibility, as usual.

2. Spice things up

However close you may feel to your partner emotionally, maybe you could do with spicing things up a little in the bedroom. Esther Perel has a wonderful book called *Mating in Captivity*,[83] which outlines how to keep desire and passion alive in long-term relationships. She describes how our quest for secure love is actually in conflict with our pursuit of passion and explains how both democracy and intimacy are passion killers in the bedroom. If you're committed to your partner but sex has become a bit *bleh*, this is a good book to start with. It offers a very different approach from that of John Gottman's *The Seven Principles for Making Marriage Work*, below.

3. Invest in your relationship

If you've let your intimate relationship slide or have drifted apart from your significant other and that's affecting your sex life, start reinvesting in both of them. John Gottman's *The Seven Principles For Making Marriage Work*[84] is brilliant for reconnecting with a distant partner. It's so easy to lose sight of the person we fell in love with after years of domesticity. Do the exercises in the book and see if anything changes. If you can, try to somehow find a balance between this book on strengthening intimacy and the one by Esther Perel, which recommends creating more uncertainty in a relationship. If you succeed, please write your own book because it will be the new Holy Grail!

4. Accommodate hormonal changes, take sex back to pleasure and experiment

My online membership has a wonderful workshop on the importance of pleasure (and intimacy), and it's so important. Take the pressure off. It's a very disconcerting fact that vaginal tissue not only gets thinner and dryer as estrogen reduces, but the vagina may also become shorter and narrower. This is particularly the case if you're not having intercourse or other vaginal sexual activity.[85] Yes, sorry to tell you this. It isn't a problem for all women, but it can make vaginal sex uncomfortable and sometimes painful. Whether or not you've given birth vaginally or how easy or difficult births were for you (for example, if you had an episiotomy and have scar tissue), it can all affect how comfortable vaginal intercourse is during and after menopause. For example, I didn't give birth vaginally, and my vagina never stretched to accommodate a baby's head. I don't find it surprising that my main menopause-related issue has been vaginal sensitivity.

Heterosexual sex doesn't always have to be PIV (penis in vagina). I love that there's an acronym for this! There's so much more to explore. "Outercourse" can be a lot of fun, too: think teenage dry humping without clothes on. Alternately, try oral or manual stimulation instead of PIV for a while, until you feel more vaginally aroused. You can take turns to give nonsexual pleasure to each other. Make it about giving and see what happens. If you both want PIV, then experiment with depth if vaginal pain is an issue. The more vaginal sexual activity you have (without the pain, of course), the less it's likely your vagina will shorten and narrow. Grab a great lubricant (see below) and give it a go.

The head of a man's penis is the most sensitive part. In other words, he can get a ton of pleasure by inserting just the head of the penis in your vagina. If you get the angle right, you can get the clitoral stimulation you need too. Chances are that will be satisfying for you both, and a lot less scary if full PIV is just too painful right now.

5. The Three-Minute Game

The Three-Minute Game[86] is a fun approach to try. It's another tool to take the pressure off and brings back playfulness. It's about giving and receiving pleasure within a time limit and sharing equally. The game is an exercise for two or more people, where specific questions are asked. The game helps partners communicate and refine their capacity to give and receive in a relationship. Get your timer out!

6. Invest in a good lubricant

A good lubricant is so important! My current favorite is Pjur Woman silicone lubricant. I used to insist on organic and liked Yes products, and even coconut oil, which can be great. But because Pjur stays on the skin and isn't absorbed, it's super smooth and lasts. It's seriously good. I have very sensitive skin and am fine with it. I use the one designed specifically for women, which I think is gentler than the original for anal use.

7. Invest in sex toys

Seriously: invest in sex toys. I first discovered them in my mid-30s and they changed my life! If becoming aroused is an issue, a small but powerful bullet vibrator directed at your clitoris may get your bits responding if they're not performing as you want them to. Similarly, vibrators can help us have fabulous orgasms with or without penetration. They're fun with or without a partner.

8. Have fun and pleasure yourself

Self-play is particularly important as we age. It keeps blood flowing to the vulval area and keeps us able to respond sexually. There's some truth to the adage "use it or lose it," as we've seen above. But "using it" doesn't necessarily mean PIV sex. If you're forcing painful or uncomfortable penetration, that's only going to cause more issues as anxiety around performance creeps in, and you get into a vicious cycle that leads to even less arousal. Keep pleasuring yourself without a partner, as well as with, if you have one.

9. Care for your vagina like you care for your face

Coconut oil can be good to moisturize your vagina. There are also several organic vaginal moisturizers on the market now, including Yes products. Be careful what you use because you don't want to introduce more chemicals into this most sensitive of areas (they could make matters much worse). Sea buckthorn oil taken as a supplement can also be helpful for maintaining the health of our vaginal tissue[87].

If there's itching and irritation of the vulva, first try changing whatever you use to wash the area. Make your cleansers as natural as possible, or even use nothing at all. If irritation persists, visit your doctor. Our vaginas can clean themselves, so never ever *ever* buy vaginal cleaning products. Similarly, if you want to use soap on your vulva, find a natural one and only use a little bit. My body soap is completely natural and made with olive oil. If I use anything else, I'm in trouble. Similarly, I switched to all-cotton undies and never plan to go back to synthetic ones, no matter how nice they may look. My vulva is much more comfortable. Something about our hormones changing makes us so much more sensitive to things that would previously not have bothered us. It's time to start listening to our bodies again.

10. Try localized estrogen

If it's just too painful to consider vaginal sex and you want that, get some estrogen pessaries/suppositories or estrogen cream. With my vagina tending towards the tight side of comfortable, I occasionally go back to localized estrogen to loosen things up a bit. From an environmental standpoint, I wish the Vagifem estrogen pessaries weren't packaged as one pill in a long plastic dispenser inside a wrapper of foil and plastic. I have no problem reusing the dispenser, but that isn't an option. I changed to an estrogen cream, Ovestin, instead, as there is only one applicator per tube rather than per dose. I feel a bit better about that. I also feel more comfortable having this localized version of estrogen, rather than systemic hormone therapy.

11. Have fun with compromise

What to do if you just don't want as much sex as your partner does? This can happen to the best of us; remember that a current lapse in interest doesn't mean a permanent one. It may just seem like too much of a bother (and there's so much else on your to-do list, right?) Enter the two-minute solution. This wonderful book, *My Spouse Wants More Sex Than Me: The 2-Minute Solution for a Happier Marriage*,[88] transformed my relationship. Sex used to be about lots of foreplay, and if I wasn't in the mood, it went on and on, as my beloved tried to get me going. I'd be back to my mental to-do list in no time—that's not just me, right? Now we just laugh, say "two minutes?" whip out the Pjur lube and away we go. Turns out I don't want a lot of foreplay very often anymore, anyway. Just give me the orgasm! Often my egg vibrator gets to play too, and we all have fun. Sometimes it turns into quite a bit longer than two minutes, and sometimes it doesn't. It also doesn't have to mean PIV sex, though it usually does. It always ends with a smile on both our faces. *The Two Minute Solution* is designed for younger couples with kids and work in the way of sex, but it works just as well for older folks too. Give it a go. What do you have to lose?

12. Try a little mindfulness

I never would've thought that mindfulness could help women with our sexual response, but it can. If we start paying attention to sexual triggers and sensations in our bodies, instead of going off on our mental to-do lists, we can cultivate more desire. If we think back to when sex was best and we were really turned on, it's likely we were completely in the moment. We can lose that focus as time goes by. *Better Sex Through Mindfulness: How Women Can Cultivate Desire*,[89] by Lori A Brotto offers advice and exercises for reconnecting with our sexual selves.

We look more at relationships and how to build and maintain intimacy in Chapter Ten.

URINARY INCONTINENCE

A word about incontinence. One in three women suffers from stress incontinence when we laugh, cough or sneeze, or bounce around on a trampoline, for example.[90] Often, incontinence starts after childbirth. It can start or get worse in menopause as estrogen levels drop, affecting the tissue in our vulval area. Incontinence is common, NOT normal. Wearing a pad to protect yourself from leaking in midlife is not a rite of passage and is only a short-term remedy. It will seriously mess with your very sensitive genital skin. If you continue wearing a pad for the next 30-odd years, you'll end up getting diaper rash! Go see your doctor, get a referral to a pelvic physiotherapist, and get treatment. Most women with stress incontinence are cured after just six sessions with a pelvic physiotherapist, as my podcast guest, pelvic physio and stand-up comedian Elaine Miller told me.[91] It comes down to pelvic floor exercises: Kegel exercises, done properly. Don't suffer. Get help. Do the exercises religiously. And get better. Elaine says your orgasms will improve, too— double whammy! Remember, leakage is common, not normal. If all else fails, localized hormone therapy can help too.

A FINAL WORD

As you can see, there's so much to try that can help with menopausal issues. Always remember, you're not dealing with a problem that affects just who you are currently. What you put in place now will keep you fit and healthy long-term. It will set you up in the most powerful way, so you can enjoy a magnificent midlife, and beyond. A word of caution, though, about all the different things I've suggested. Don't assume any single one of these is going to fix everything. Often, it's a package of things that will do the trick.

For me, it's organic soy and soy milk; ground flaxseeds daily; no dairy milk; no caffeine; trying to limit sugar, alcohol, and processed foods; running; yoga; meditation; a great lubricant; sex toys; and my friends. Having good friends you can fall back on makes all the difference. It helps to remember none of us is alone. Everyone who has (had) a uterus will go through menopause—that is, if we're lucky enough to live this long.

Hopefully, you'll have a better idea now of what areas need attention in your life and some immediate options to try out if menopause is getting you down. I hope you'll realize the changes you're experiencing have all sorts of implications and may need more than hormone therapy to get you to optimal health and well-being. Helping you achieve these long-term, as well as creating the next chapter of your dreams, will be the focus of the rest of this book.

Not only can we women suffer during menopause, especially initially when we don't understand what's happening to us, but our menfolk can get mighty confused too. Here's a helpful little explanatory letter for you to show to the man in your life.

A LETTER TO THE MAN IN YOUR LIFE

Dear man in my life,

I've been reading this book and it's really quite illuminating. The author suggests I let you read Chapters Four through Seven especially, to give you a bit more of an idea of the changes that are happening to me in midlife. Turns out I was a bit uninformed about menopause. I thought it happened in my mid-50s; actually, my hormones started to change in my mid 40s! No wonder I've been feeling a bit off.

Perhaps you could think of it as puberty in reverse. It's not something that happens overnight, but it can make me a bit emotional and grumpy, and perhaps sometimes seemingly a little irrational. Bit like an adolescent, really. I discovered there are certain things I can do to help myself transition vibrantly through this time. You may see me making changes to my diet, trying to up my exercise, cutting back on caffeine and alcohol, perhaps, and other changes. I really want your support, and if you want to make similar changes, I'm sure it will be good for both of us health-wise for the long term.

I had a more negative perspective on menopause before starting this book. I'd bought into a lot of the negative stereotypes about the end of my fertile years and getting older as a woman. I'm learning that it's an exciting time of transformation for me, and I really hope you'll embrace coming along with me for the ride. I'll be different, both during this period and when it ends, because I'll have a different hormonal profile. Eventually, I'll be off the estrogen roller-coaster, meaning you may get a more emotionally consistent me than you've had in the past.

Please don't think of this transition negatively, but instead, see me as a butterfly emerging from a chrysalis. I'm excited about what's to come. There may be a few bumps along the road ahead. You may find I'm more anxious for a while. I may be grumpier than usual. I may put on a bit of weight and feel a bit sad about that. You may need to be more gentle and creative when it comes to our sex life, as my vagina may change along with other things. But I'm excited about the fun things we can explore together as our life evolves.

One of the most interesting things I've learned by reading this book so far is that whales also go through menopause and then become the leaders of their pods, often for up to 50 years. This really helps me see that far from being over, my life is now getting rather exciting. In fact, I now realize I may live at least half my life without messy periods, which is rather cool. I hope you'll understand if I appear a little more self-centered. It will take some time for me to process this transformation and work out who I'm going to be in my next chapter.

Thank you for reading this. If you want to read more of this book you can borrow it when I've finished. Please give it back now!

Your loving woman xx

CHECK-IN

Write down the answers to these questions in your notebook or journal.

How are you doing hormonally?

On a scale of 1-10, with 1 being "dismal" and 10 being "great," how would you rate each of these areas?

1-10

- Menopause experience in general
- Emotional well-being
- Stress management
- Diet
- Exercise
- Weight
- Possible exposure to toxins
- Sleep
- Sex life
- Overall happiness

If you've not scored very highly on any of these, what can you do to score better?

What do you feel are your priorities for improvement from this list?

What three small action steps can you instigate to improve your hormonal balance?

PART III

INTO THE FUTURE: CRAFTING THE NEXT CHAPTER OF YOUR DREAMS

CHAPTER EIGHT

BUILDING LONG-TERM RESILIENCE IN BODY AND MIND

"Aerodynamically the bumblebee shouldn't be able to fly, but the bumblebee doesn't know that so it goes on flying anyway."
Mary Kay Ash

This book is about making midlife magnificent, not just better. You need to be strong physically and mentally to reach your full potential in your next chapter, not retreating into some dingy corner, not accepting the status quo of your life, unless you feel it's already magnificent. Instead, showing the world your light and finding real joy in what you do. This section is where we start deepening your resources and resilience so we can ensure you're the strongest you can be, to make the very most of your exciting life ahead. We'll look in more detail at what you need to have in place long term to enable you to thrive.

GETTING FIT AND HEALTHY LONG TERM

Much of what we've already discussed to create health and well-being during menopause is completely applicable long term. You can't go back to how you lived before menopause once you're on the other side. Maintaining optimal hormonal balance and fitness must be a long-term activity if you want long-term health! The dietary and stress management changes you make for menopause are what you need long term. You'll still need your cardio, stretching, weight-bearing, and lifting exercises. Working to maintain your balance will also be ever more important as you age.

Lifting weight is often the element of fitness most missing from our midlives, but it is very important. An easy way to start doing this at home is by watching a good YouTube video and using some resistance bands (or cans of beans!). In *Fat Around The Middle*,[92] Dr. Glenville suggests doing two or three 30-minute sessions of weight/resistance training each week, with time in between to give your muscles a chance to recover and repair themselves. Take great care with your technique. You don't want to injure yourself while trying to improve your health. It may be worth hiring a trainer to advise you on technique when you're getting started. Dr. Glenville says the best time to exercise is early in the morning as this is when the body is most inclined to burn stored fat. She advises having some sort of protein (nuts or a tuna salad) within half an hour of exercise, whether that is aerobic or weight training. The protein feeds the muscles used during the training and helps to restore them. If you're not already doing much exercise, I know this sounds like a lot. But remember, this book is about becoming magnificent, not mediocre. It really pays to invest now in your future health.

If you can run, that's good for your heart health and for building and maintaining bone density. It's also great for stress relief. You could get yourself the Couch to 5k app and give it a go. Many women worry about running, fearing problems with their knees, hips, or any other part of us that may hurt when we run. But this doesn't necessarily mean we shouldn't be running. It's more likely to mean the way we run isn't as good as it could be, or that there's some imbalance in our bodies. That same BBC documentary about menopause I mentioned earlier looked at three groups of menopausal/postmenopausal women: one doing no exercise, another doing exercise but not running, and the third running. It was the third group, the runners, that had the best bone density score. If you do take up running, know that moving in a straight line is less likely to have a negative impact on our knees, for example, than rapidly changing direction. This is why footballers tend to suffer more from knee injuries than professional runners.

But we need to take heed of any aches and pains, as that is our body trying to tell us something, though not necessarily that age is the reason. We've talked a lot about rejecting ageist narratives, dismissing the idea that life is one big decline from midlife, assuming you can't be as fit as you were when younger, or that your beauty fades with age. Staying curious about actual changes to your body and their causes is crucial if we're to avoid making the classic mistake of attributing changes to age when they're actually nothing of the sort. This is particularly the case with aches and pains. So don't ignore aches and pains, but don't assume they're automatically part of life now either.

If you can't run for whatever reason, try cycling, rowing, fast walking, bouncing on a mini trampoline, or swimming to get your heart rate up regularly. You may also want to invest in a Fitbit to keep track of how many steps you take each day.

It's a good prompt for movement. I really notice a difference the day after if I haven't done my target of 10,000 steps. I'm sluggish and have more aches and pains, not fewer. And my clothes fit a bit tighter.

It's really important to stay mobile throughout the day. I once interviewed Katherine Allen, author of *The Qigong Bible*,[93] on camera. She had an alarm set to go off every 30 minutes to remind her to stand up and move around, including a full body shake (which she expected me to do too). She didn't tell me her precise age, but I know she's in her 70s, and she could lift her leg above her shoulder. I didn't stand a chance of competing with her level of flexibility! Qigong[94] and its sister tai chi[95] can do wonders to help you stay flexible and mobile into your later years. They are well worth trying, whatever your age.

You may also want to take time to assess your posture. I've known for a long time that my poor posture and sedentary life led me to have very stiff hips and hamstrings. Lots of running can exacerbate this situation. To do more exercise, I need to do more stretching or yoga to counterbalance. Our bodies don't bounce back as easily as they once did. But the more exercise and stretching you can build into your daily routine, I believe, the better you'll feel. Just be sure to warm up gently and listen to your body about what is possible!

For a while, I added orthotics in my shoes to help with heel pain before discovering SockDoc,[96] who says we should only ever use these if there is a medical necessity. In the same way that hormone therapy masks issues associated with menopause, he believes that by changing the way we move, orthotics mask pain that needs to be dealt with. Our feet are perfectly designed to move us around, but we insist on limiting their natural mobility with heavy, inflexible shoes, which rarely match the natural shape of our feet. I've now invested in some minimalist Vivobarefoot[97] shoes and am finding these great, not only for my feet, but also for my overall movement and posture. I reckon my hips and balance are already improved by radically changing the way I walk. So if you suffer from foot or leg pain, it might be one option worth exploring.

I've also discovered a whole new approach to joint health. I tried all sorts of things to fix my piriformis syndrome,[98] including releasing pressure in my buttock by sitting on a hard ball. Fitness specialist Tom Morrison has a completely different approach to this kind of pain, his Simplistic Mobility Method.[99] He suggests that we think less about the individual muscles and more about the joint itself. He recommends moving our hip joint, for example, through its full range of motion on a regular basis to stop the pain that will come from both inaction and overcompensation for pain. His approach was a revolutionary concept for me, and I'm finding it extremely helpful. Check out Tom's videos on YouTube for a wide range of drills to help with joint mobility.

If I didn't make it clear enough already, it's often a good idea to start a regular yoga practice. Start with something easy like Hatha yoga. I reckon it will enable you to live longer with greater flexibility and without pain more than anything else will. Midlife is the time to make exercise a habit if you haven't before. In her excellent book, *More Than a Woman*,[100] Caitlin Moran talks about how, in midlife, she was tricked into doing yoga, having fought against it for years. She's now hooked, loves it, and feels a bit silly for not embracing it sooner. Moral of the story? Don't be like Caitlin! Get yourself a yoga mat, find an easy video to follow on the Internet, and get on the floor. *Yoga with Adriene* on YouTube[101] is a great place to start.

LOOKING AFTER YOUR BONES

Generally, careful impact on our bones makes them stronger, which is why it's important to include some form of exercise that includes impact on our bones, as outlined above. As we age, our bones don't rebuild themselves as well as they did when we were younger. We also lose some of the protective element of estrogen post menopause. In their excellent book *The Age-Well Project: Easy Ways to a Longer, Healthier, Happier Life*, Annabel Streets and Susan Saunders talk about how to reduce the risks associated with osteoporosis and highlight smoking, alcohol, low body weight, and genetics as all having an impact. Fortunately, there is lots we can do to look after our bones, starting with diet. Annabel and Susan write:

"Calcium intake is also crucial. Ninety-nine per cent of our calcium is in our bones, but popping a pill is not necessarily the answer. Research shows that our bones absorb dietary calcium better than calcium from supplements.[102] How, then, do we get dietary calcium? It's wrong to assume that dairy products are the only source. Bony fish such as sardines provide good levels of calcium. And it's perfectly possible to get all the calcium we need from plant sources. Calcium finds its way into plants from the earth, ending up in dairy products because cows eat plants. The calcium in plants is easier for our bodies to absorb than the calcium in milk. Brassicas such as pak choi, kale and broccoli are rich in calcium."[103]

Alliums (onions, garlic, leeks, and the like) are also recommended because, like brassicas, they are a source of a compound called sulforaphane, which has been shown to help build strong bones.[104] The nutrients we need for bone health include calcium, vitamins B12, D, C, E and K, magnesium, boron, folate, and isoflavones.[105]

The Menopause Manifesto[106] has a detailed chapter all about bone health. There's also a free online tool, the Fracture Risk Assessment Tool (FRAX),[107] designed by researchers at the University of Sheffield in the UK to give an instant assessment of fracture risk. This can't provide a complete picture, but it can be a good place to start with understanding your personal bone health.

GETTING ENOUGH REST

Rest, and most importantly, sleep are crucial aspects of getting and keeping you strong for your next chapter. Once your hormones have settled down post menopause, you may find sleep is no longer an issue, but for many women it remains a problem area. Sleep is so important, I felt it warranted some extra attention here. Matthew Walker, professor of neuroscience and psychology, and director of the Center for Human Sleep Science at the University of California, has written a fascinating book called *Why We Sleep: The New Science of Sleep and Dreams.* In it, he says that short sleep duration predicts short life. Scary, huh? He found that adults 45 or over who sleep less than six hours a night were 200% more likely to have a heart attack or stroke compared with those sleeping seven or eight hours.[108]

Insufficient sleep increases blood pressure and stress levels, so your heart rate increases. It's bad for you. It's also linked to how we deal with stress. But if you're completely on top of stress management and on a zen cloud all day long, you're probably not going to suffer, even if you don't get a full eight hours' sleep. Let's keep this in proportion. The last thing I want is for you to get stressed about getting enough sleep and lie awake worrying about it!

The longer we sleep, the more chance we have of getting the right quality of sleep too. We sleep in cycles of about 90 minutes and these shift from one stage to another, both of which we need. The early stages of sleep are dominated by non-rapid eye movement (non-REM). As we sleep longer, we shift into the deep slow-wave sleep phase, which is dominated by rapid eye movement (REM). If we don't go to sleep early enough, we limit our non-REM sleep. If we wake too early, we miss out on REM sleep, that period when our most vivid dreaming usually happens. It might be worthwhile to avoid watching any overly stimulating or scary TV before you try to wind down into gentle restful sleep! Remember your getting-to-sleep routine.

Make sure you also allow enough time for the sleep you need. If you need to get up at 7 a.m. and you're aiming for seven to eight hours of sleep, make sure you're in bed by 11 p.m. at the latest. If you know it'll take time to drop off, or you're likely to wake up and struggle to get back to sleep, try going to bed even earlier. The Tapping Solution[109] app, mentioned earlier, has some great meditations to help with both getting off to sleep and achieving deep sleep. The Calm[110] app has lovely sleep stories for adults.

As mentioned earlier, if you're lying awake, don't forget to try meditating (count to 10 over and over or repeat a mantra in your head) or listen to a sleep meditation on your phone. Try Insight Timer,[111] but don't get caught up in messages or social media at the same time. If thoughts are keeping you awake, try to ignore them. But don't turn getting back to sleep into another task! The harder you try, the harder it will be. Like many things in midlife, it's all about letting go.

Many people believe technology, such as mobile phones, tablets, and modems can impact sleep. I slept in our living room, where there's a modem and a big TV, for several nights. I didn't sleep well. It could have been the streetlight outside or the technology, or something else, who knows. But I think it's worth trying everything, so if nothing else is working, try removing technology from where you sleep.

PROTECTING YOUR BRAIN

There's still so much we don't know about the brain and mental health. A brilliant book on female brain health is *The XX Brain, The Groundbreaking Science Empowering Women to Prevent Dementia*, by Dr. Lisa Mosconi, which I mentioned earlier when talking about stress and menopause symptoms. It's no surprise that stress also massively impacts our brain health. Dr. Mosconi writes,

"Perhaps more than any other health risk, stress is the silent killer our society has yet to acknowledge fully. Those of us in the health field already recognize it as a major contributor in all leading causes of death, including heart disease, cancer, lung disease, and Alzheimer's." [112]

She says gender differences in how we process stress—overwork, the way caring responsibility devolves to women, and modern life in general—make women particularly prone to suffering and getting ill as a result of stress. She says it's crucial we take steps to reduce or better manage stress if we don't want our brain and mental health to suffer.

I've talked about meditation, yoga, and journaling to help relieve stress. Taking time for friends and social interaction is also key, as shown by how crucial tight community is thought to be to the longevity of people in the Blue Zones, those parts of the world where people live the longest and are the healthiest. Making sure to have down time away from work and when we really switch off, is particularly important for brain health. So is swapping out screen time for time in nature. Try a little mindfulness to keep you grounded and your mind from racing.

Dr. Mosconi also suggests a particular kind of singing meditation, which has been tested in women with a dementia diagnosis, Kirtan Kriya (KK). She writes:

"KK prescribes practicing the specific sounds 'Saa Taa Naa Maa' accompanied by mudras, elegant finger positions, for just twelve minutes a day. This short but sweet practice has been shown to reduce inflammation while improving memory, sleep, and overall well-being in people with average cognition, as well as in patients with mild cognitive impairment. In one study, participants experienced improved mental clarity and up to a 50 percent increase in memory skills within eight weeks. A pilot study by the Alzheimer's Research & Prevention Foundation (ARPF) investigated the cognitive impact of KK on 161 women at risk for Alzheimer's, including some experiencing forgetfulness, some with a diagnosis of mild cognitive impairment, and others under pressure due to their caregiving roles. After two to four months of training, those who practiced every day showed increased blood flow to several parts of the brain, as well as improvement in their overall cognitive function. Wouldn't it be wonderful if a better memory was ours merely by singing for twelve minutes each morning?"[113]

Just search YouTube[114] for a video showing you exactly how to use KK.

The XX Brain has lots more tips for how to protect our brains through diet, supplements, exercise, sleeping enough, acupuncture, and more. Other great books which cover all aspects of aging well, but especially the brain, are *The Age-Well Project*[115] by Annabel and Susan, and the follow-up book, *The Age-Well Plan*[116] by Susan (who herself has the Alzheimer's gene).

Finally, a note on staying intellectually active. Learning new things and staying engaged in the world are massively important for long-term brain health.

Dr. Mosconi again:

"Brain imaging studies also revealed that lifelong participation in cognitive activities, such as reading books and newspapers, writing, playing music, or joining a chess or card club, had the power to slow down and perhaps even prevent Alzheimer's plaques. Particularly impressive is evidence that even in patients carrying mutations that cause Alzheimer's, a higher educational level was associated with a delayed onset of any cognitive decline."[117]

Some recent software and apps that claim to help train our brains have actually been found to do little for us. So be curious and open about what will help. Dr. Mosconi says the important thing is to learn *new* things to challenge your brain. If you're good at chess, playing more won't help, but learning a new game will. Taking up new hobbies, learning new languages or skills, learning to play a musical instrument, joining a book club, being social, and playing games will all help. I spent the COVID-19 lockdown teaching myself how to play *sudoku* and have tripled the speed at which I can do the puzzles. Yay!

I also like to deliberately follow commentators and read arguments I don't agree with. As we age, it's easy to get stuck in our own way of thinking. I really saw that with my own father. As always, staying curious about the world and ways of thinking keeps our brains active and enables us to avoid getting stuck in dinosaur land. Interacting with young people and listening to their thoughts on the world, in particular, is a brilliant way of keeping our minds active. Being challenged in our thinking keeps us vital and engaged with the world. Curiosity may have killed the cat, but it can definitely help us live longer and more vibrantly!

BUILDING CONFIDENCE

Stepping into our magnificence usually requires confidence, but this can all too often start to disappear as we get older, for all the reasons we've already discussed. I want you to feel strong and confident, now more than ever, especially as we start to create your magnificent next chapter. So let's take a moment to look at some steps to improve your confidence.

Imposter syndrome seems to be the buzzword of the day, and it's totally governed by our brains too. Women, especially, suffer a lot from this in midlife, when we can often forget or dismiss the skills and experience we've accumulated. And what's the peak for imposter syndrome for women? Menopause![118] No surprise there. This is particularly the case if we've spent years at home looking after family. In general, women are taught not to brag. My British generation was taught to be modest, to put others first. Thank goodness my stepdaughters have moved beyond that. Sometimes their attitude is hard to accept, but I reckon it'll stand them in much better stead than the self-deprecation I grew up with.

Men rarely have problems putting themselves forward, but women are often more reticent. The fear of being found out for not having the necessary knowledge, experience, or skills to do whatever is required, can be enough to hold us back. I say enough with that! We're too far along life's path now to let anything hold us back.

Thinking back to how CBT can be used to reframe hot flashes, we can use similar techniques to build confidence. Changing how you talk to yourself can be a radical act of self-care. We often talk much more harshly to ourselves than we would ever to a friend. So, take some time to catch your thoughts next time you think badly of yourself or when your confidence plummets and your negative inner voice says, "told you so." Ask yourself, "is that really true?" Try to turn a negative thought into a positive one. Over time, the more we think new thoughts, the more they translate into new neural pathways in our brains. Thoughts we've created can become what we believe. By imagining that we're confident, we can make our brains believe we really are. Our brains will believe pretty much anything we tell them. How's about that for power? But it's a conscious choice you need to make. What you focus on will also increase; our thoughts create our reality. So it pays to really be aware of where your thoughts are lingering. Do you focus on the positive or the negative?

What are some quick ways to improve your confidence if it's fallen off a midlife cliff? If that's where you are, don't beat yourself up about it. Without confidence, we can find ourselves curtailed from much of the best stuff life has to offer. Lack of confidence can cause us to doubt our relevance and leave us questioning our value in the world. I don't want you to go back there again, so we need to tap into our own ability to increase confidence. If need be, trick yourself into feeling more confident.

TIPS TO BOOST YOUR CONFIDENCE

Emotional

- Make a list of at least seven of your positive attributes (those you believe about yourself and what others tell you).
- Look in the mirror and tell yourself positive affirming statements (I am...).
- Take time for yourself to restore and replenish your energy every day.
- Journal to release any fears and dream about what you want more of.
- Put little reminders about how great you are or your affirmations throughout your space or on your phone.
- Say "thank you" when a compliment is given—no deflecting.

Physical

- Look in the mirror and strike a power pose, especially before a confidence-needing encounter.
- Sit or stand straight; no slouching.
- Smile, the kind with your eyes crinkling (because those are genuine).
- Breathe deeply.

TIPS TO BOOST YOUR CONFIDENCE CONTINUED...

- Wear colors and outfits that make you feel confident. Think about updating your style if you feel you've got into a bit of a rut.
- Incorporate exercise into your daily routine.
- Use music to lift your spirits and dance about to an energizing and encouraging playlist. Listen to it whenever you need a boost or are inspired to do so. (On one podcast where I was a guest, the host decided my theme music should be "Queen of Clubs" by KC and the Sunshine Band. I now put it on Spotify whenever I need a little confidence boost!).
- Remember that external confidence is a result of your positive internal voice, combined with a positive mindset.

Positive Internal Voice + Positive Mindset = External Confidence

Remember, too, that post menopause, you'll hopefully feel more confident than you did while your hormones were messing about.

CHECK-IN

Write *down the answers to these questions in your notebook or journal.*

- Hand on heart, how physically fit do you feel? How is your emotional/mental health? What can you do to improve these?
- How mobile are you during the day? What can you do differently so you don't get locked in the sitting-down box?
- What can you do to help your bones remain healthy?
- Do you get enough rest? How can you prioritize sleep?
- What can you do to protect your brain health long-term?
- How confident do you feel? What steps can you take to increase your confidence?

CHAPTER NINE

EXPLORING POSSIBILITIES FOR YOUR FUTURE

"Life shrinks or expands in proportion to one's courage."

Anaïs Nin

MIDLIFE THROUGH A NEW LENS

I hope by now you're seeing the true potential in midlife (and beyond). The further I've got into this period of my life, the more excited I've become about the possibilities. It's such an interesting and enjoyable phase. It's the absolutely perfect time to take a new blank canvas and play with what we want for the second half—because midlife is exactly that, the middle of life. You hopefully have as much time ahead as you've already had. If that doesn't seem possible, you still could have another 30 years ahead of you if you're 50 now, and just think what you achieved between 20 and 50 (30 years). There's no reason you can't achieve something similar, if not far more, in the next 30 years because you now have wisdom and experience on your side.

If you've already encountered my podcast, you'll know I've interviewed some fabulous and yet also regular women doing amazing things in midlife. When I say, "amazing," that doesn't have to mean big or dramatic. It just means they're doing something that lights them up, that gives them a sense of creating something meaningful and feeling more fulfilled. It's not too much to talk about creating a legacy. Because when we get to midlife, we become more aware of our mortality (remember the Death Clock?) and our thoughts often turn to legacy. We want a sense that what we're doing matters, that we're not just treading water.

Hopefully, you're now on the way to getting any issues sorted. You're building an arsenal of strategies and tools so you can capitalize on the strength that's innately yours but which may have been hidden and overwhelmed by the necessities of day-to-day life. Now's the time to start thinking about what may be possible in your next chapter.

As I've said, I believe the first half of our lives is actually just the rehearsal. I spent most of the first half on a metaphorical treadmill. I did what I thought I was supposed to do, and I didn't really question that much. Being truly intentional and having a plan for my life was not something that occurred to me; I'm not sure why. I think perhaps I was just never encouraged to dream big. Maybe you were the same. There's a trajectory we seem to go on in the first half. We go to school, some of us go to college, we start work, we often find a life partner, some of us have children, children leave. Then what? Menopause also kicks in, we're suddenly very aware of that ticking life clock, we may flounder around a bit, and we think, *what on earth am I supposed to do now?*

Most of us don't have a plan for the second half. Traditionally, there was education, work, maybe family, and then retirement. But life doesn't work like that anymore. Some of us may never be in a position to fully retire, and many of us simply don't want to. What are you hoping to do in terms of retirement? What can you do? As life expectancy increases, so do the number of years we potentially have available to fill, hopefully with more of a life we enjoy, whether or not we have the financial security we need. Those extra years aren't necessarily added on at the end of life when we're no longer in our physical and intellectual prime either. Rather, those extra years come in midlife, as we extend the years when we're still potentially physically and mentally as good as we can be.

Along these lines, in the *Middlessence Manifesto*, Barbara Waxman says,

"...according to an article appearing in the medical journal *The Lancet*, more than half of all babies born in industrialized nations since 2000 can expect to live into the triple digits. Midlife doesn't begin until we're in our 40s, and with advances in medicine and our ever-increasing knowledge of healthy life-style habits, the life stage carries on well into our 60s."[119]

The traditional way of thinking, that years are added to the tail end of our life, and we're therefore older longer, is no longer applicable. In my mid-50s, my life is very different from that of my own mother at this age. I'm not slowing down as women were (and sometimes still are) expected to do. I completely refute a recent research study that found our get up and go starts to decline at 54.[120] Poppycock! I'm not coasting towards retirement, whatever that might be. I actually feel like I'm just getting started. Those additional years have been added in the middle of my life, rather than at the end. Yippee!

THE POWER OF THINKING DIFFERENTLY

Hopefully, we can still enjoy a good level of health if we look after ourselves for many years to come. I feel better positioned to make the most of this second half because of who I am now. I've come to terms with what it means and looks like to be an older woman, and I've found that I like myself more now than ever. I feel more confident of my abilities and my power. I've built a support network around me that's cheering me on from the sidelines, that has my back when things don't go quite according to plan, and that will keep me moving forward. I also have more time and space now to think about what I really want. I'm not on autopilot anymore. Now that my son is gone, I have fewer financial commitments than I've had for a long time, and I have a burning desire to make a life that's right for me. I want that for you too.

Clearly, building this new life may not feel like an option for everyone, because many of us don't have the financial security to enable it. Writing this in the time of COVID-19 and a re-invigorated Black Lives Matter movement, I'm aware of my privilege to still be able to think in terms of self-actualization, not just fighting for social justice or keeping a roof over my head. But none of us has infinite resources or a perfect scenario in life. We're all fighting battles other people know nothing about. Life can change in an instant. I hope to demonstrate that there are ways to make our lives more magnificent, even with the constraints under which we may find ourselves.

If you're still feeling stuck in the messy middle, battling with everything midlife throws at you, don't worry because you're only part way through the book. We've so far been focusing on getting the basics sorted. Now we begin to think about possibilities and how you can start creating more of the life you want. I hope you'll get increasingly excited about what can be possible.

Because of all the change, midlife is the perfect time to start reviewing our lives and strengthening our foundations. As we start listening to our bodies more, we can also start questioning our thoughts. It took me until my late 40s to realize that just because I think something, doesn't make it true. The early menopause pushed me to start questioning all the stories I believed about myself. That prompted me to start questioning pretty much every thought I had. I've touched on this before, but how we think and what we believe have an enormous impact on what is possible for each of us.

Viktor Frankl was a German psychiatrist who spent five years in a Nazi concentration camp. In his book *Man's Search for Meaning,* he wrote, "everything can be taken from a man but one thing: the last of the human freedoms—to choose one's attitude in any given set of circumstances, to choose one's way. And there were always choices to make."[121] I love the idea that every thought is a choice.

In much the same way as I suggested you could trick yourself into feeling more confident, I'd like you to regularly question your thoughts, and especially any limiting beliefs, like those thoughts and opinions you have that stop you from moving forward. Be aware of what you think day-to-day. Catch yourself if you think, *I'm too old to do this*, or *I'm too old to wear that*. Be curious about why you have those thoughts. Where did they come from? Can you pull them apart and establish whether there is any credibility in them at all? If there's something you want to do, but you've already discounted your ability to do it, revisit it without those limiting beliefs. We've already seen that how we feel about aging affects how fast we age, both mentally and physically. So really try to be aware of your thoughts each day. Keep a journal to note them down.

The whole premise of a wonderful book, *The Art of Possibility*[122] by Benjamin and Rosamund Zander, is to think about all the things that may be possible without any limitations. It provides a toolset to enable you to think in a way "unfettered by reality." My husband started giving copies of it to everyone! I recently gave one to my son. It's the book I wish I'd read 30 years ago. Back then, I was still living my life in a straitjacket. I didn't know I could imagine and potentially create many different kinds of life for myself. As I've gotten older, I've come to accept that our thoughts really do create our reality. Do your best to think thoughts that are going to help you move forward, rather than hold you back, so you can become who you were always meant to be.

There's a follow-up book to *The Art of Possibility* called *Pathways to Possibility*,[123] which is equally illuminating. If we're open to possibility, we can recreate ourselves whenever we like, if we're willing to change our mindset. In this second book, Rosamund Zander writes:

"You can change your story at any time to be better adapted to the magnificent flow of the way things are, and the world will reflect the change in you, opening doors and showing you a path to where you want to go and what you want to do. This outlook gives rise to joy, love, and gratitude, leaving room for fear only in circumstances where feeling fear will mobilize you best to avoid an immediate threat to life and limb—a truck bearing down on you, for instance; not the prospect of losing someone's affection or being fired from your job."[124]

Years ago, I'd have thought this idea, that just by changing your thinking your life could change too, completely "woo woo." Experience has taught me to be more open to the power of my own thought in molding my life experience. To see how effective your thoughts can be, you just need to see how positive thinking and visualization are used by top athletes to help them secure gold. We can all create new realities. We all have every right to want to create a life that is meaningful for us. So, I'd like you to start thinking about what you want from life and who you want to become. In the spirit of the art of possibility, I want you to open yourself up to absolutely anything.

THE POSITIVE SIDE OF FEAR

Sometimes, just starting to think outside the norm can bring on anxiety. If you're starting to feel nervous about where I'm leading you, take a deep breath and remember that fear is excitement without breathing. I love that description, which has been attributed to several wise people. Fear and excitement occupy the same area in our brain alongside our inner critic (but we'll talk about her later). Here's a powerful quote when it comes to fear, from Marianne Williamson, that illustrates how we're most likely kidding ourselves about what lies at the root of our fear:

"Our deepest fear is not that we are inadequate. Our deepest fear is that we are powerful beyond measure. It is our light, not our darkness that most frightens us. We ask ourselves, who am I to be brilliant, gorgeous, talented, and fabulous? Actually, who are you not to be? You are a child of God. Your playing small does not serve the world. There is nothing enlightened about shrinking so that other people will not feel insecure around you. We are all meant to shine, as children do. We were born to make manifest the glory of God that is within us. It is not just in some of us; it is in everyone and as we let our own light shine, we unconsciously give others permission to do the same. As we are liberated from our own fear, our presence automatically liberates others."[125]

If you don't believe in God, swap in whatever works for you (universe, the world, Mother Nature, or something else). It's all good. I think this quote goes to the heart of what so often stops us in life. How exciting to embrace that we can be powerful beyond measure (even on our own lunchtime). I think hesitancy often stops us, because of the messages we've learnt about keeping ourselves back, staying modest, never bragging, and prioritizing others over ourselves. But why put any brakes whatsoever on our own limitless potential? We go back to my desire for us all to live up to our potential for ourselves, but also because the world desperately needs more women to do just that.

So we have to learn to do it anyway, despite the fear. To feel it, move through it, and ultimately put fear in its place. I like the way Elizabeth Gilbert describes her approach to fear in her book *Big Magic: How to Live a Creative Life, and Let Go of Your Fear*:

"Fear: I recognize and respect that you are part of this family so I will never exclude you from activities, but still—your suggestions will NEVER be followed. You're allowed to have a seat and you're allowed to have a voice, but you are not allowed to have a VOTE. You're not allowed to touch the roadmaps; you're not allowed to suggest detours; you're not allowed to fiddle with the temperature. DUDE, you're not even allowed to touch the radio. But above all else my DEAR old familiar friend, you are absolutely FORBIDDEN to drive."[126]

Just imagine what you could do if you were absolutely fearless. Fear isn't bad. It can keep us safe. But it can also limit us massively. For that reason, think of it also as a sign we don't yet have the right information or resources to enable us to do the thing that's making us fearful. We can fix that. In today's world, we can learn absolutely anything online. There are so many free resources we can tap into to teach ourselves anything at all. So if you're feeling fear, embrace it and keep moving through it.

UNDERSTANDING YOURSELF

By the time we get to midlife, we're different from the way we were when younger, and it's easy to lose sight of who we really are. We can downplay aspects of our personality, our strengths, and our innate need for a greater sense of purpose, when all of these aspects can help us evaluate possibilities for our future. We're going to look at these different aspects now, so you can build a greater understanding of yourself and what makes you tick.

1. Your strengths

A good place to start when evaluating possibilities and where you might go next is to understand your strengths. Self-improvement often focuses on our weaknesses. How much more exciting and empowering to establish what our strengths are and build on those. Most of us have little sense of our core strengths, much less the ability to build our lives around them. When we know our strengths, we can add this knowledge to the melting pot, to enable us to work out where we'll feel most comfortable in the world. I'm not talking about superficial strengths, such as our baking ability or how many languages we speak. This is about our innate strengths, such as consistency, ideation, communication, self-assurance, and others.

There's an online test called the Strengths Finder,[127] originally developed from over two million interviews conducted by Gallup. You answer a number of questions and are then given your top strengths from a total of 34. When I did this test, it completely blew my mind and radically changed the direction of my life. Since then, what I've created is perfectly aligned with my core strengths. The key concept is that when we build on our strengths, we excel, and that will necessarily make us happier.

My five top strengths, in order according to the test terminology, are ideation, input, empathy, belief, and connectedness. If you're fascinated by ideas, love discovering what lies beneath, and enjoy looking at things from a new angle, then ideation is probably your strength. Input is all about how inquisitive you are and how much you like acquiring things or information that interests you. Research is a joy to me, and I've loved finding all the information I share with you here. Empathy is fairly self-explanatory, but if this is you, it's important to be in an environment in which you can express it and certainly not where to do so would be out of place—such as when I worked in the tough and usually self-serving world of financial communications.

Belief means that your core values affect your behavior and give you meaning and satisfaction. If what you do conflicts with your values, that's not an environment in which you can thrive. I reckon this strength of belief becomes stronger as we age. We'll be looking at values later on. Connectedness is also linked to a sense of responsibility and values. If this is your strength, you'll probably like building bridges and communities and bringing people together. Building the magnificent midlife world has brought me great joy, as I'm building a global community and connecting women who might otherwise never have had that connection.

I recommend you do the test and explore your strengths. There's a free version of a similar test at high5test.com,[128] but I prefer the Strengths Finder. By the time you've paid for the detail with High 5, they're roughly the same price anyway. If you're not happy in your work, it's possible you're not working in alignment with your strengths. The test can't help you identify a specific job you'd be happiest/most effective in, but it can help you evaluate a role to see whether it plays to your strengths. This is another of the tools I wish had been available in my youth. While all our experience leads us to now, I'd likely have been much happier in a career that played to my strengths. In midlife, when we're working out what we want for the next 30 years, the Strengths Finder can offer an illuminating process to help us.

2. Your personality

Many of us want to be more authentic in midlife. We want to be true to ourselves and not put up with things we no longer like or agree with. But often we go through life unsure of who we really are. As well as understanding your strengths, it's also valuable to understand your personality better. There's another online test you can do for free to find out your personality "type." Myers Briggs[129] personality testing enables you to get a really good feel for why you move through the world as you do. After you do the test, you end up with four letters. Each of these letters has two alternatives (indicators), so there are 16 distinct personality types. The individual indicators, developed by a mother and daughter team, are based on Jungian theory and describe our personality preferences. Preferences include whether we focus on the outer world or our own world, how we process information, how we make decisions, and how we interact with the outside world.

I did the test a few years ago and found it incredibly illuminating. I had an idea I was probably an introvert and always felt rather an outsider compared to other people. I wasn't particularly shy and assumed I had to fit in and have lots of friends. I expended a lot of effort trying to achieve that, with very poor results. I wish I'd known it was okay to look inward rather than outward for my main source of energy, which is an introvert's predominant characteristic according to the Myers Briggs test. I wish I'd known that needing my own space didn't necessarily make me weird. Over time, I realized I wanted to have an impact and that my intuition was very strong. It turns out my Myers Briggs categorization of INFJ makes me pretty damn introverted, very intuitive, somewhat emotional, quite judgmental, and pretty rare. A psychotherapist once cautioned me against adopting the label and therefore excusing myself. She had a point. But I've found it really liberating to understand more about how I interact with the world. If this is something you haven't already done, I really recommend this test too.

Midlife is a great time to increase your self-knowledge and acquire more tools, so if you went down pathways that didn't fulfill you before, hopefully your chances of avoiding that will be better in the future. Self-knowledge can also be incredibly helpful when life doesn't go according to plan and you have to pivot. Hattie Voelcker had a long career as a family law barrister until illness meant she could no longer do that job. She was forced to change careers, and by tapping into who she really was and what her skills were, she was able to create a whole new and more fulfilling career for herself. She is now a performance coach working with singers, and she sees many similarities between her role as a barrister and the one she has now, but with skills applied differently. She was a singer in her youth and has tapped back into that ability in her new career. She can also see how her years as a barrister in the court room were not that dissimilar to any performance on stage. She says,

"I spent the first part of my life trying to prove myself, working hard and doing a job that had a lot of kudos but a lot of stress. Eventually this proved too much, and I became ill. This allowed me the space to realize there was a different way of living a successful life, one that was way more enjoyable!"[130]

3. Understanding your sense of purpose

What do you need to feel happy? What do you need to feel fulfilled? We'll look later at relationships and emotional input. Now, I want you to think about where your own inner life is going. How important is it for you to have a sense of purpose? As we get older, we often get clearer on what really matters to us and have less time for the things that don't. I love the clarity I now have about how to spend my precious time. I'm still learning, but I'm getting better at saying no. I'm aware, as I've said before, that I have less time left than I've already had. I don't want to waste any more of it.

Our ultimate sense of well-being is often found at the place where fulfillment and contribution meet. If we contribute without feeling fulfilled, we'll likely feel resentment. Many of us want to give back more the older we get, and it's difficult to achieve a sense of fulfillment without contribution. Through my 30s and 40s, I was increasingly uncomfortable with my lack of contribution to the world. I still had to pay the bills, so that had to be my main priority. But feeling I wasn't contributing became more and more challenging for me. What, exactly, was my purpose?

Author Dan Pink[131] talks about the difference between Purpose with a capital "P" and purpose with a small "p." It's easy to get a bit scared of the word Purpose. It can feel a bit all-consuming and overwhelming. Do we have to change the world to express our Purpose? Of course not. Many different activities can help you find more purpose. It might be you start volunteering one morning a week in your local school. It might be you start jotting down your thoughts in a journal. Whatever your purpose (or purposes) turn out to be, they will be perfect for you.

Along these lines, Barbara Waxman cautions against getting too obsessed with finding the "right" purpose. She writes:

"I believe that purpose is such a big and lofty concept that it often obstructs what's right in front of us. When we focus solely on finding purpose, we can limit our vision and ability to move forward. The truth is that more often than not, our purpose finds us. It evolves when we live in sync with our values and grow to know ourselves more fully. We can also have more than one purpose. And purpose can change over time. . . Everyone's purpose is different, so there's no right answer to the question of where to find it. Purpose is simply whatever brings you the greatest meaning or joy."[132]

Your purpose will evolve throughout life, just like you do. We can change our own world, we can have an impact on a friend, we can have an impact in our community. All of these are valid expressions of purpose and can make a considerable difference to how we feel about the contribution we make. Purpose doesn't need to be big or grand. Whatever works for each of us is what's important. Sometimes it's easier to think about living purposefully than finding an elusive, concrete purpose. But some form of purpose is good for us. Recent research has shown strong associations between having a purpose in life and better physical health and well-being down the road. Using data from the health and retirement study at the University of Michigan, Eric Kim and colleagues found that:

"People who report high levels of purpose at one point in time have objectively better physical agility four years later than those who report less purpose. There is even a dose response—meaning, for every jump in purpose scores, people were 13 to 14% less likely to experience physical declines in grip strength and walking speed."[133]

I find this remarkable. There is such a clear correlation between one's own sense of purpose and one's physical well-being as we age. Intuitively, it's something I completely understand, but to have it confirmed by research is extraordinarily powerful. Having a sense of purpose has been found to provide better cognitive functioning, greater longevity, and even basic characteristics like better dental health! Kim suggests that when we have more of a sense of purpose, perhaps we see the importance of our goals in life and, therefore, take better care of ourselves. Whatever the reason, it really brings it home how important that sense of purpose is, whether with a capital "P" or a small "p."

Having a sense of purpose can also help us manage stress and anxiety better. When we're young, for instance, it doesn't matter much whether our sense of purpose is directed towards ourselves or the greater good of society.

But as we get older, the most beneficial purpose is one beyond ourselves. Several years ago, I started doing small voluntary efforts to fulfill my need for purpose. These had an immediate impact on my personal sense of well-being. I spent a couple of years using my public relations skills to raise the profile of an environmental campaign to get shops to close the door when using heating or air-conditioning. Then I decided I wanted more personal impact, and I volunteered each week in a local primary school, reading with the children. The more I did this kind of thing, the more I wanted to do it, until I created the Magnificent Midlife world, moving ever closer to making my passion and purpose my full-time gig.

If you're feeling a need to do something, and you're not sure what, start exploring volunteer opportunities in your area. Even something small can have a big impact on your own sense of self-worth and whomever you're helping. A good place to start is asking yourself: "What am I good at?" "What skills do I have that could be of use for a cause?" and "What do I care about in my community or society?"

Then, if you decide you want to change the world, you can always put a capital "P" on the front of your Purpose and see where that takes you! If this appeals right now, think about what really bugs you. If you had a soap box in Times Square or at Speakers Corner in Hyde Park, what would you use it to talk about? What would you most like to change about the world? What most annoys you? That's a good place to start when considering where you might put more energy.

A RETURN TO CREATIVITY

It's worth remembering, too, that we have our second creative peak in our 50s. I loved finding this out. It's great to have random ideas corroborated in print! It doesn't surprise me, especially for women. Many women report a surge in energy post menopause, and that happens mostly in our early to mid-50s. As I've said, I found the end of my fertility to be my most creatively fertile period yet. Many women find that their need for creativity really kicks in around midlife and the absence of an outlet for it can cause real discomfort.

Some women also report feeling more like their prepubescent selves post menopause, without so much estrogen running the show. Their creativity was unrestrained back then. Because of this, it can make sense to look back to your childhood and consider what lit you up and inspired you then. Chances are you might still find those things interesting now. I played piano for many years after puberty, but I stopped just before my final exams at school. Something had to give, and it was piano and my other instruments that lost out. I did a lot of singing in my teenage years too but gave that up at college.

When I was going through this process of exploring things I'd enjoyed in my past, I started tinkering on the electric piano bought for my stepdaughters. Much to my father's delight, I started singing again. Both have been fun, and the singing has led to all sorts of exciting things I could never have dreamed of. My husband still nags me about the saxophone hidden in a cupboard upstairs. My excuse is that it's just too loud to practice in an urban apartment. Maybe one day.

Before I get you to contemplate your own world of possibility, here's another story about a wonderful woman called Jo Moseley. I featured Jo twice on my podcast[134] with the episodes less than a year apart. That's because she'd accomplished the most incredible amount in less than a year, and I just had to get her back. Jo's creativity in midlife has shown itself in building a whole new "side" life for herself. I first encountered her on social media where she was sharing her own mini adventures. She shared how she'd suffered from depression after a difficult menopause and grieving the death of her mother. Her mini adventures, generally involving some kind of physical activity outdoors, transformed how she felt about herself and brought back joy. The main thing she discovered was her love of stand-up paddle boarding, often on the open sea. It was the UK North Sea, so it was bloody cold! She also likes scrambling up hills and anything to do with water, including regular swimming. Jo doesn't consider herself at all sporty, but she realized getting out in the open air regularly was incredibly good for her mental health.

When I first interviewed Jo, it was about her work to persuade similarly stuck women in midlife to get out and exercise. But Jo didn't stop there. She announced she'd set herself a challenge, to stand-up paddle board from one coast of the North of England to the other, 160 miles through canals and rivers, from Liverpool to Goole. When I interviewed her the second time, she told me all about this remarkable achievement. She was the first woman to do it, and she accomplished it at the tender age of 54. She was featured in many national newspapers and magazines as well as on the BBC. She's since been featured in a film about it. It wasn't long before Jo was being invited to speak all over the place to share her inspiring story that started with her crying in the biscuit aisle in a supermarket and ended with her triumphantly reaching the east coast on her paddle board.

Jo's story is a remarkable one of self-belief after extreme self-doubt. She found the courage and curiosity to do something far outside her comfort zone, which ended up inspiring the world as well as herself. It strikes me as the epitome of the art of possibility. Jo still has a day job, but she's managed to completely transform her life. Her secret weapon? Self-belief. Imagine what it could do for you if you start with just one small step.

POSSIBILITY EXERCISE

PLEASE READ THIS - EVEN IF YOU CAN'T
ANSWER THE QUESTIONS RIGHT NOW!

I want you to get out your notebook and get creative. Just do some free writing here. Don't write what you think I want you to write. Just let your hand take over and lead you down the garden path of inspiration! Set a timer for 20 minutes to start with and repeat as necessary/desired. But just let your thoughts take over as you answer these questions:

- What are you really good at?
- What makes your heart sing, that you gladly do for free?
- What are five things that excite you?
- What lit you up when you were young?
- When did you feel most full of purpose in your life?
- What would you like to revisit if you had no limitations?

- What are you curious about?
- How would you spend your time if money were no concern? What would you love to do?
- What can you happily rant about, and why? What would you use a soap box to talk about?
- What upsets you in the world? What do you most want to change about the world? Why?
- What five things would you like to be remembered for after you die? Why?
- In 10 years' time, what will you regret not doing?
- If you were to die tomorrow, what would you regret not having done?
- Where are you compromising?
- In an ideal world, what do you never want to do again?
- What part of life now do you not want to continue? It could be a long commute, living where you live, the job you do, eating asparagus, anything.
- Create a "chuck it" list.

W1t you've written? What are the themes? Write those down too. This is where the clues to your dream future lie. Does your "chuck it" list make it easier to narrow down the direction you'd like to take? Can you live your purpose and passion more? I hope so!

Wow, you've covered a lot in this chapter. Now I want you to set all that aside as we move to the next section. We'll revisit this work in Chapter Eleven, when you'll actually get to plan your magnificent next chapter. Now I want you to let your thoughts and ideas percolate and see what bubbles up from your subconscious.

Next, we're going to look at what you might want to change in your life so you can start living with more purpose, passion, and joy. We'll examine what to keep and what to let go, so you can create that future.

CHECK-IN

Write down the answers to these questions in your notebook or journal.

- Can you identify two limiting beliefs you have? Can you let them go or reframe them?
- How does fear show up in your life?
- What are your top strengths from the Strengths Finder test? How aligned are those with how you live your life?

- What does your Myers Briggs personality profile tell you about how you interact with the world?
- What do you think would give you more of a sense of purpose in life?
- How does creativity show up for you?
- What revelations did the Possibility Exercise bring up?

CHAPTER TEN

GETTING HONEST ABOUT LIFE

*"Life's ups and downs provide windows of opportunity
to determine your values and goals. Think of using all
obstacles as stepping stones to build the life you want."*
Marsha Sinetar

This book is mostly about embracing the positives of midlife
and our menopause transition. To be able to do that fully,
we also need to look at any negative aspects of our lives,
what you might call the shadows. Shadows play an important part in who we are. Midlife and menopause are when we
say goodbye to one stage of our lives while welcoming in
another. If we fail to acknowledge the shadow side of who
we've been and who we are, we can risk that holding us back
in the future. Menopause has a message in the word itself:
Me. No. Pause. I see it like this: Me relates to learning more
about yourself; No suggests knowing what to let go of that
no longer serves you; and Pause suggests giving yourself
time and space to deal with unresolved issues and mark your
transition. We benefit from admitting to our traumas and, if
they're so dark as to still be impacting us, asking ourselves
what we need to do to make them less so. In this chapter,
we'll look at some of the areas you may want to assess before
you move on to creating your future plan.

EVALUATING YOUR PAST, PRESENT AND FUTURE

Arvigo therapist Hilary Lewin[135] taught me how important it is to proactively deal with our shadows in midlife while also marking our menopause transition. We can do that by evaluating the different phases of our life and the shadows within each, taking a good, honest look at what we want to take forward into the next chapter and what we want to leave behind.

1. The three phases of womanhood

When you look at mythology, there are three distinct phases to a woman's life: the maiden, the mother (or what Hilary calls the creatrix), and the crone, or wise woman. I have an innate dislike of the word crone. It suggests the three witches boiling up trouble in the first scene of *Macbeth*! But traditionally, it has meant "wise woman" as much as "sorceress." Traditionally, as the maiden, we were the responsibility of the elders above us who directed our lives. The creatrix years are about creating a family, a home, a career, and finding value in the eyes of society. Then, in the third stage, we become the wise woman, and life is more about us. We care less about what others think—and that's the joy and glory of being a postmenopausal woman! We wear what we like and do what we like because we no longer care what others think of us. We can become more whale. That's the hope anyway.

But we've already seen how issues we haven't dealt with can raise their ugly heads around midlife. If we choose to, we can look at some of the shadowy aspects of our lives and process those now. Maybe we've put aside unresolved issues from our youth or more recent times because we had to get on with making life work. Those issues likely haven't gone away, and it pays to take the chance midlife gives us to unwrap and reevaluate them, or maybe take them to a therapist but deal with them as we transition.

2. The importance of retreat to process our shadows

Retreating and giving ourselves time to do this shadow work becomes very important. Doing a retreat is all about getting you in the best possible emotional state to move forward in your magnificent midlife. You can get the diet sorted, the supplements in place, the exercise plan working and even your confidence up. But if you're still holding on to emotional baggage that can hurt you, then you're not making the most of who you've been, who you are now, and who you can become.

In an ideal world, we'd take ourselves away and do a real mid-life retreat. But for many of us, that's just not possible. You may still have little ones at home or teenagers dealing with their own hormonal challenges. Double hormonal trouble! Maybe work is mad and elderly parents demand attention too. As a result, taking yourself away for some quiet retreat time may feel completely impossible, but it's still necessary. Get creative about carving out the time you need. You can even do your retreat simply by taking a long hot bath with the door locked; do this as many times as necessary to enable you to process whatever it is you need to process. There are ways and means of making a retreat happen, whatever your circumstances.

Whatever the logistics of your retreat, Hilary recommends splitting it into the three phases of your womanhood and taking as much time as you need on each. It doesn't all have to be done at once, but do take the time to go through this process. Start by thinking about your maiden years. What did you like about that time, and what did you dislike? What would you like to take forward into the next stage, and what would you absolutely like to leave behind? Perhaps there was joy, playfulness, or confidence in that time of your life that you've subsequently lost. Perhaps you can try to bring those back with you into the next phase of life. Is there anything negative still haunting you? Now's the time to deal with it and hopefully let it go.

Next, take time to evaluate your creatrix years. What's been good, what less so? What lessons do you want to treasure? What still hurts and, therefore, needs to be processed and let go? If menopause is bringing up more grief around being childless, for example, try to deal with that. What do you need to forgive yourself for? Who else do you need to forgive? What are the strengths you discovered in these years? What do you want to take forward? What lessons do you want to share?

Finally, take time to consider who you want to be in your wise woman years as well as your hopes and dreams. It's time to start saying "no" to things that pull on you but no longer serve you. What is the darkness in your life and your responsibility for how things have shaped your experience? How have you responded to what life has thrown at you? While you're considering all of this, also take time to mark the transition into your next phase. Light some candles or a bonfire. Have a little ceremony. Really celebrate who you are and all that you have achieved.

Shadow work is thrust upon us in midlife, whether we want it or not. If we choose to engage with it, through retreat work or getting help, it'll become that much easier to heal and move forward. Like anything, if we hide from it, deny it, and just try to soldier on, it'll come back to bother us and may even translate into sickness later on.

3. The importance of status

When we look at long-term health and our likelihood of being diagnosed with medical conditions and diseases, increasingly it's being found that status is a huge part of our overall health. This isn't about how big your house or your car is, but about what personal power you have, your sense of agency too. Look at the degree of status in your life. Do you have status/power in your relationship, in your family, and at work? How has your status evolved through your maiden and creatrix years? If you still don't have the status you need, you may be being bullied, and if that's happening in one area of your life, you may find it's happening in another area too. What can you do about that?

Hilary also says the biggest step we can take to improve our overall health is finding a way to improve our own self-judgment. A status check as part of our retreat work is an important thing to do. It's about identifying where you have power and whether you're making the most of your power. Where are you holding on to power too much, and where are you giving it away? By considering all these questions, we can take back or create the power we need to move forward and thrive.

As our bodies go through this massive change in midlife, we need to take time to mark the passage and appreciate what it means for us. If we do this process well and start talking about how to do midlife and menopause constructively, we'll have an incredibly positive impact on ourselves and also on the women coming up behind us. Now's our chance to start changing it for the women who will follow on, for our daughters, nieces, friends, and even our granddaughters.

4. Processing unresolved issues

The retreat process will likely bring up any unresolved issues you have. Emotional baggage can take up a lot of head space and stop us from reaching our potential. If we're preoccupied with issues from the past and still expending energy on those, how can we possibly make the very most of our future? While you're doing this process of retreat and reevaluation, consider anything from your past that still causes you pain. It might be difficult relationships in your birth family, problems in your career that still haunt you, grief or loss you haven't fully processed, or humiliations or deceit that can still trigger you. Dealing with these issues is often much easier said than done, however. I have things in my life I'd love to be able to sort out but still don't seem able to. Years of psychotherapy have taught me if I can't deal with an issue when I've really tried, it's better to just let it go rather than allow it to continue causing pain.

There are some things in life you really can't do anything about. You can't change people; you can only change yourself. So perhaps it's about putting on your armor and becoming Teflon woman. Or spending enough time meditating on a particular issue, exploring its nooks and crannies, and finally saying, "Begone, you annoying bit of twaddle!" Perhaps you write your issue on a piece of paper and then have a symbolic burning ceremony to release its foul stink to the universe.

5. Use journaling to process thoughts and feelings

Writing things down really does help. This is where the idea of journaling comes into its own. For years, I was skeptical about journaling, but I finally saw its value and am now an aficionado. It can be helpful for finding out what your inner self really feels, processing emotions, and managing difficult issues. I try to write regularly, sometimes just free writing or else with a series of prompts. Sometimes, I just pick up my notebook when I have an issue bothering me. I find it helpful just writing all the rubbish down! Doing a regular gratitude and forgiveness practice is also hugely empowering.

Here are the journaling prompts I use to get my daily writing moving if it needs a little help. These were inspired by business coach Gemma Went:[136]

- I choose to release
- I choose to receive
- Three affirmations (e.g., I am strong, I am centred, I am healthy—three things you want to be or have, expressed in the present tense)
- I forgive
- I am grateful for
- Future me visioning (envisioning who you're going to be or what you'll achieve.)

The more you simply let your hand move across the paper without too much control from your brain, the better. This is where pen and paper really do work better than a keyboard. My writing is atrocious, and I can type faster than I write. I even bought a book on how to improve my handwriting! I also don't much like wasting paper. Even so, I've discovered the very real connection between our thoughts and our hands as the pen moves across paper. There's science to back this up, too — writing by hand activates parts of the brain responsible for learning, memory, healing, and related activities.[137] Having to make my writing legible so I can read it later has also forced me to slow down, which is no bad thing when trying to process ideas in my head! So get out your notebook and pen, and start writing!

EVALUATING YOUR RELATIONSHIPS

It's not surprising there's an increase in wife-initiated divorce in midlife.[138] Menopause puts a strain on many relationships; we're different after menopause, both physically and emotionally, and our needs, wants, and priorities can all shift dramatically. I see women approaching their future at midlife in two main ways. Some women accept the life they have, rationalizing to themselves that it's okay and that change would be too difficult. Other women are willing to take a long and sometimes cold look at where they've ended up, stay curious about what's ahead, and start taking steps towards creating the life they want, rather than the one they've ended up with. I'm guessing you're in the second camp!

It's also important to evaluate our relationships at this time. They need to work for us now and into the future, and we may need to build new ones.

1. Your intimate relationship

My first marriage broke down in my early 30s, after the birth of my son. I left because I knew there had to be more to married life. As I started this book telling you, I desperately wanted another child. By 35, I was a single parent, trying to find a nice new man to make a baby with me. That wasn't to be, but the process of going through a separation and then divorce taught me a lot about how resilient I could be in the face of trauma.

I was lucky enough to meet a wonderful man who's now my husband. Still, we've had our issues. Building a family that works for two sets of children is one of the biggest challenges of my life. But if push comes to shove, I'm never going to be a martyr in my personal life again. I have the strength to know I can survive on my own if I need to, and I can create my own happiness. It's crucial to realize we're responsible for our own happiness and acknowledge that happiness is often a choice. We also need to love ourselves before we can love anyone else effectively and in a healthy way. Just because you've always been in one particular relationship, doesn't mean you always have to be. Similarly, if you're alone now, that doesn't have to be your future.

But, and it's a big BUT, I'd urge you, if you're in a relationship—under no circumstances—to walk away from it during your menopause transition without first doing some serious work to salvage it if need be. Menopause, declining libido, and a dry vagina can put a lot of pressure on heterosexual relationships. I've also heard of lesbian relationships where only one partner was going through menopause, and the other was distinctly unsympathetic. Often physical issues are symptomatic of deeper problems within a relationship. Make use of your curiosity to consider the background to issues and take proactive steps to fix these before you decide to make big changes. Here are some things to consider.

i. Being open to taking some responsibility

The Art of Possibility has a number of tools to reevaluate our perspectives on life. For me, one of the most powerful ones was the tenth practice, "Being the Board."[139] Without having read the rest of the book, this may be a tricky concept to get, but it's incredibly effective, so stick with me. It's basically imagining that your life is a board game and instead of being one of the players, you are the board itself. When faced with a very difficult situation to which there seems no solution, you ask yourself how this situation arose in the game, of which you are the board. How did the stalemate come about? It enables you to take the sting out of a particular situation and look at the whole environment as well as your role in that environment. It takes away the aspect of blame and encourages greater curiosity and power of analysis. It may also open you up to your own role—after all, we know it takes two to tango.

I'm still practising this technique, but I find it useful to help me stop and think about a situation in a completely new way. It has definitely opened up the possibility for me to acknowledge some responsibility where previously I was too angry and hurt to even contemplate doing so. As I've said, curiosity is a powerful thing!

ii. Being proactive about love—it's a verb as well as a noun!

Another book I've found incredibly powerful for dealing with issues in intimate relationships is John Gottman's *Seven Principles for Making Marriage Work*.[140] I referenced it in the section on menopause and sex earlier on, but it's so good, it's worth consulting at least twice! This groundbreaking book is based on research that found how easy it is to predict relationship breakdown based on how couples communicate from the start. It's a fantastic guide to changing the destructive patterns that so many of us have perfected by the time we reach midlife. Each of the seven principles has exercises that immediately open lines of communication with your partner.

The book is centered on increasing the knowledge we have of our partners, nurturing fondness and admiration for them, connecting with them regularly and authentically, accepting their influence, solving solvable problems, overcoming gridlock, and creating shared meaning through shared rituals and habits. The book introduces The Four Horsemen (communication styles), which are the biggest predictors of relationship breakdown. These are criticism, contempt, defensiveness, and stonewalling; and there's lots of advice on how to make sure they don't become fixtures in your relationship.

I think this book is amazing. I soon realized that stonewalling was a big issue for me, as I can get overwhelmed quickly by conflict. A suggestion here is to take a break until tempers have calmed down, and you can approach the conversation in a calmer and less emotional state. I've used this technique in the past to get my own emotions back under control.

iii. Getting real about physical intimacy

When we experience intimacy problems in our main relationship, there can be myriad issues at play. We've looked at how menopause can impact our libido and cause significant changes in our vaginal tissue. In addition, I want us to look at emotional aspects of any issues before looking in more depth at sex. Often, by the time we reach midlife, we may have been in a relationship for 20+ years, perhaps even longer. It can be challenging under any circumstances to maintain a level of sexual passion and excitement in any long-term relationship. Like any aspect of a relationship, it takes work. I cautioned earlier that if your libido isn't what it used to be, it might not necessarily be menopause at play. Maybe you're just a bit bored or have resentments that are impacting how warm and fuzzy you feel.

We've looked at how maintaining sexual activity, solo or partnered, is generally very good for us. The pressure to perform can often serve to put the brakes on our bodily response. *Come As You Are*[141] by Emily Nagoski is a great book that analyzes in-depth how men and women differ in their sexual responses, how we can get better aligned, what makes women tick, and how and why that's the case. If you're in a loving relationship but have stopped having sex, this book is a great place to start.

There are ups and downs in all our sex lives. When we strip out any element of shame, we can get back to fulfilling intimacy. Emily explains that aspects of our lives and relationships can hit the brakes for us sexually. The short answer to the question, "how to stop hitting the brakes?" is "Reduce your stress, be affectionate toward your body, and let go of the false ideas about how sex is 'supposed' to work, to create space in your life for how sex actually works."[142] The long answer is the entire book, which I highly recommend.

Physical intimacy is important. You didn't get together with your significant other to be their sister or their friend. You're in an intimate relationship. If you both conclude you no longer want sex in your lives, that's entirely up to you, although I'd still urge you to keep reading and potentially reevaluate that decision. It's really worthwhile to put effort into sex, just as you put effort into any other aspect of the relationship. I read once that when sex is good in a relationship, it's a relatively small part of that relationship. But when it's bad, it becomes the entirety of that relationship. If you're less bothered about maintaining sexual intimacy than you were in the past, apply curiosity to figure out the reason behind that. Make sure you're on the same page as your partner; otherwise, you're on a road to heartache for at least one of you, if not both. I guarantee your intimate relationship will be more fulfilling if you can be happily sexually intimate. Don't forget the two-minute solution[143] if you genuinely want less sex than your partner or just want to take the long, drawn out pressure off your pleasure.

As I've read more about sex, I've learned it can be many different things. Unfortunately, we tend to get stuck in the traditional heterosexual notion of penis in vagina sex. As we've seen, when PIV causes pain, this necessarily affects our sexual response, makes us fearful of intimacy, and can put a very significant brake on sexual desire. But that doesn't have to mean the end of all intimacy between you. Work out what's going on, how interested you are in getting back to where you once were, and what you currently need, want, and desire in all aspects of the relationship. Think about that for your partner too. If you don't, they may be the one heading out the door.

If you've done the work on all aspects of your relationship and still can't see yourself staying where you are, by all means, make whatever choice you need to enable you to live your best life. But be aware that the person you fell in love with still exists, even if it's difficult to find them. It's worth taking a good look to see if you can find them again before you head off into the big blue yonder. I'm just playing devil's advocate here—the one you know (with some work to smooth the rough edges) may be better than the one you don't. Please don't let your relationship or physical intimacy be things you decide to leave behind in midlife without first doing some work to understand how they got to where they are, how you might fix them, or the consequences of a future world in which they don't exist.

2. Friends

As my life has evolved, I've met wonderful women doing similar things who've become firm friends. These women are my new support network. I have long-standing friends who also offer me support and other friends I rarely see and with whom I no longer have that much in common. It may sound a bit harsh, but I see nothing wrong with letting friendships lapse if they no longer serve you. We change, often quite dramatically. When that happens, our wants and needs become different, especially if we embrace this time of transformation rather than trying to fight it in favor of staying the same. This means we're likely to be drawn to different people. Many of us make our closest friends at school or college. If you're a mum, you probably found your children brought new friends to you. I made some of my closest friends when I moved to New York and enrolled my son in nursery. At the time of this writing, he's 23, and I still count some of the friends I made then among my closest.

Building my business has connected me to amazing entrepreneurial women. They have been instrumental in sustaining my enthusiasm, sharing frustrations, and celebrating successes along the way. These newer friends have almost exclusively been made online. I've traveled to visit them, and we've gone away together. I met my husband online, so I'm very open to building relationships this way. It's nice to know friends can also be made in the digital world.

You may have already found you have less in common with your lifelong friends. Don't be scared by this. It means you're still growing, changing, and, hopefully, developing into the person you were always meant to be. That said, it may mean you need to seek out new friends. You needn't let your old friends go entirely, but perhaps you can adjust to not having so much contact with them. You may also find, of course, that as you grow and change, your long-standing friends (or your life partner) don't like the new you. Sadly, this situation can happen when we try to change. Friends and family may try to pull you back to the version of you that's familiar to them. Remember crabs in a bucket. One tries to get out, and the others pull it back. Your friends and family may simply be trying to keep things the same so they don't have to feel uncomfortable.

Make sure you have the support network you need to live the life you want. Don't be afraid to reduce negative energy, even if that means seeing less of lifelong friends. Be there for them if they need you, and you them. As well as being a lifelong learner, become a lifelong maker of friends. I didn't make a lot of friends at school nor at college and have gone through life since then collecting interesting female friends. They may not be very numerous, but they are truly wonderful, and I feel very fortunate.

You can find new friends by pursuing new interests—a class in real life or online, for example, an activity like pottery or language classes, or even an online membership. Maybe attend a conference on something that interests you. But be sure you don't just sit back. Be proactive about making new contacts and follow up with them afterwards. The new friends I've made have almost all come from taking the same online course, which also had an online community. I reckon if I can do it, anyone can, because I really don't find it easy to make new friends! As it turns out, some of my newest friends are some of my closest.

BECOMING AWARE OF PATTERNS

By midlife, we've likely established patterns of behavior that may no longer serve us very well. We've looked at how ageism begins between our ears and the impact that can have. When going through your "getting honest about life" process, consider behavior patterns that may do more harm than good. For example, many of us struggle with taking our rightful place in the world and expressing difficult opinions because we were taught to be the good girl: humble, modest, and not rocking the boat or blowing our own horn. If we want to step into a magnificent midlife and beyond, where we find and deliver our passion and purpose, we need to find our voice and do away with patterns that hold us back.

In *Pathways to Possibility*, Rosamund Zander writes:

"I believe that when we become aware of patterns in our behavior, when we learn to identify and rewrite the stories that give us our identities, we will gain passage, at any age, into a new phase of adulthood. In this territory of maturity, where old fear-based patterns no longer hold us back, we will, I wager, do what we now think of as remarkable, even magical, things."[144]

I get goosebumps just writing that down on the page! As I've become braver and more open to change, the world has shifted in my favor. The more I step forward into my new magnificent world, the better life becomes. Rosamund says we may assume there are limits as to how much we can grow and change, whether we can change others and even the world at large, and how much freedom and joy we can experience. When we start dismantling these assumptions and see them for what they truly are—just assumptions we've made—we can become much more powerful. Often our thoughts and behavior are made rigid by difficulties in childhood, and then these patterns continue as we get older. Now we've arrived at the stage of giving zero fucks, we can throw all those old patterns out with the bathwater and create new behaviors that fit where we are now. How exciting!

Be curious about patterns that hold you back. Perhaps you have a belief that originally came from your parents, and if you analyze it carefully, you'll find you don't really believe it. Perhaps you never did. Let it go. Perhaps you're still too concerned with what others think about you. It's easy to see how this pattern began in childhood, and as women, we're taught to be good, nice, and beautiful for others. Midlife is a time to throw all that away. It's time for you to be you, however you want to be.

Rosamund talks about the difference between living in a child's mind and in an adult's. The stories we tell ourselves often belong to the child's mind, when we would be much better served by adopting narratives that belong in an adult's mind instead. An important part of finding pathways to possibility is to identify the child's stories and ditch them for more adult ones. She writes,

"When you find yourself ready to bolt from a relationship, or hanging onto one that is going nowhere, or frightened about the future, or feeling insecure in a group; when you are driving people crazy with your efforts to get things under control, or are unable to take steps that would obviously be beneficial, or are avoiding criticism of any kind, think this: *you are living in a story made up by a child.*"[145]

Isn't that powerful? I know that's absolutely what I do. But if we can identify which of our own behaviors, patterns, and narratives are long since redundant, we can create new, more adult ones that will propel us forward to new and greater things.

EMBRACING THE EMPTY NEST

An empty nest can be hard, but it's also such a gift, given to us when we're best able to make the most of it. Whatever lives we've lived, whether or not we've worked outside the home or been a full-time mom, it can often be a tricky adjustment when children leave. They may leave temporarily, coming back at college holidays, or the move may be permanent. Our whole world can shift. I think it's easier if we have work, to be honest, as we have another role to which we can cling when the pain of our children leaving kicks in. I work from home, so I have something to keep me occupied, but I also miss my son's presence in the place where I spend most of my time. We must be able to let go of our children. If we've done our work well, they've been enabled to fly. Our relationship with them will forever be different once they are adults.

During my son's teenage years, I struggled to keep up with the speed of his development and emotional distancing from me. I knew this was what he had to do to survive as an adult. I had my empty nest strategy planned. I saw the warning signs in early adolescence as he sought his independence. I have stepchildren, but they don't live with me, so they've always been separate. I knew that for my own sanity, having focused most of my caring on my only son, I needed a plan. I started Magnificent Midlife when he was still at school.

I'm delighted I managed to find something about which I'm passionate as my other great passion flew the nest. If this is you and the empty nest is either impending or you're sitting in the middle of it, not knowing quite what to do, take some time to work out where you go from here. This is your time to shine. It's the time to really step up and make that magnificent midlife. Your children will remain crucial parts of your life, but they're adults now, and you need to let go of the part of your relationship in which you mother the young child. They may push further away from you if you can't learn to interact with them adult to adult.

If you never had children, midlife is still a big time of reckoning and working out what's next. We're going to build a plan for capitalizing on your empty nest (or just the amazing next stage of your life) in Chapter Eleven.

DEALING WITH REGRET

If you haven't already got the message, now is absolutely the time to let go of regret—that's an important part of the retreat process I covered earlier. By the end of this book, I hope you'll be raring to create whatever dream you've been incubating, possibly unknowingly, all your life. My aim is that you'll have the resources and self-belief to enable you to be and do whatever you want. There may be stuff you regret from the past, and if this still has an impact on you, write it on a piece of paper and burn it—whatever you need to do. For some women who've found themselves involuntarily childless, for example, midlife and menopause can be another time when the grief of dreams lost comes back with a vengeance. As others are moving on to new stages but still with children in their lives, the pain of having to completely give up the dream of children can be overwhelming. If this is you, take the time you need to process this new stage of your grief. Don't deny it. Feel it and work your way through it.

If things happen in life that cause you regret, try to process those as they happen rather than holding on. Also, don't let fear of regret stop you from changing your life. It will be better to regret things you've done than things you've not done. If you're intentional about what it is you want to do, are able to process hiccups along the way and pivot if needed, there will be little to regret anyway.

Soon we'll look at a future visioning exercise and explore all the things you'd like to do. We'll look at a bucket list and again at your "chuck it" list. We'll establish what you may regret not having done on your deathbed. We'll do this so you'll know exactly how to eliminate any future regret by getting on and doing all those things.

PRACTICING FORGIVENESS

Before we start building your magnificent plan, take an honest look at any resentment you may still carry. Like unresolved issues and regret, resentment can eat into your head space, allow the persistence of negative behavior patterns, and waste a lot of energy. Resentment is like swallowing poison and expecting the other person to die. It does nobody any good whatsoever. Holding grudges steals our capacity for joy. A forgiveness practice as part of your journaling will help you process any lingering resentment.

While writing this book, I discovered the Hawaiian Ho'opo-nopono[146] practice of reconciliation and forgiveness. This is a very short meditation on accepting responsibility and expressing repentance, asking forgiveness, expressing grati-tude, and love. Apparently, it doesn't really matter what you express repentance, forgiveness, gratitude, or love for. What matters is the act of saying the words in your head: "I'm sorry, please forgive me, thank you, I love you." It certainly has a calming effect!

The Buddhist loving-kindness meditation can also help to do away with resentment as well as building self-love. During the meditation, you focus benevolent and loving energy towards yourself and others. This meditation guides you first toward loving and accepting yourself, then people you care about, and ultimately challenges you to also apply this technique to people you find difficult. Meditation guru Jack Kornfield has a lovely version of this on his website.[147] It's well worth trying.

I've done my best in this chapter to cover key themes that you may want to evaluate during your retreat work in midlife. It can be immensely freeing to go through this process and let stuff go. I'm not saying this is easy, but without consid-ering the more negative, shadowy aspects of our lives, we will struggle to really step into our magnificence. There will always be something pulling us back.

In the next chapter, you'll create your next chapter plan. Before we do that, take a look back at your notes so far and honestly try to answer the questions below.

CHECK-IN

Write *down the answers to these questions in your notebook or journal.*

- How might you set aside some time to mark your evolution from creatrix to wise woman?
- Where do you have power? Where do you hold onto it too much? Where do you give it away?
- Are you happy with your intimate relationship? What can you do to make it better/more satisfying? Do you want to prioritize building one?
- Do you enjoy physical intimacy? Does this satisfy you, or could it do with some improvement? If it's not currently a part of your life, can you change that?
- Are you happy with your friends? Do they provide the pleasure and support you need as you transition into your magnificent next chapter? Would you like new friends? Which actions can you take to bring new friends into your life?
- Are there unresolved issues in your life that you need to fix or ditch? What will you do to resolve them?
- Have you identified any behavior patterns that don't serve you anymore, and can you work to banish those?
- If you're in an empty nest, are you coming to terms with that? What are the opportunities you see that might come from this?

- Are there things you regret? How can you let those go?
- Is there anyone you need to forgive (including yourself)? Practice Ho'oponopono or the Loving-Kindness Meditation to begin the process.

CHAPTER ELEVEN

CREATING YOUR
MAGNIFICENT MIDLIFE PLAN

*"Tell me, what is it you plan to do with
your one wild and precious life?"*
Mary Oliver

The previous chapter may have been hard for you. It can often be a lot easier to ignore the tough stuff, rather than excavate it. But I hope you found the process worthwhile. The reward is that now you get to create a plan for your Magnificent Midlife (and beyond)!

I've learned that if I really want to do things, I need to think hard about them, write stuff down, create a plan, draft a timetable, outline some specific goals, and get some accountability. Without some sort of framework and accountability to keep you on track, you're likely to find every excuse in the book not to do what you want to do.

For some, the concept of goal setting and adding a deadline can lead to exactly the opposite of what we hope to achieve—paralysis instead of action. Be honest with yourself. If goal setting as a concept doesn't work for you, if setting a deadline means you retreat into fear and paralysis, then don't do it. Think instead in terms of at least setting some intentions for your next chapter and having a plan to take you forward in achieving those. Don't stay stuck out of fear.

In her book *Playing Big*,[148] Tara Mohr talks about the fear we disguise with procrastination, when it comes to actually going for our dreams. It's easier to stick with the status quo. We've been taught to play small, to accept our reality, to avoid risks and not push ourselves forward. Goodness, I know all about that. Writing this book and putting my words out into the world has been deeply scary, and my procrastination muscle has been flexed throughout!

We've looked at why we don't want to accept life as it is, regardless of the consequences or blocks in our way. If we're to live our best lives, we need to pull our finger out and make things happen. Because if we want life to be different, we have to take action. Nothing is going to change unless we make it change. As I've said, I'm not in the business of making your life a *bit* better. I want it to be MAGNIFICENT! I want you to look back and think, *yes, reading this book was the catalyst that pushed me into creating a whole new magnificent existence.* The second half is when we stop allowing happenstance to dominate and what we WANT is finally allowed to take pride of place.

But a word of caution before we begin working out what's next. Whatever has already come out for you through reading this book, and whatever you decide when you've completed this final chapter, don't forget that life at any stage is a journey. There's no ultimate destination and absolutely nothing wrong with changing your mind. Since I started my midlife adventure, I've changed tack multiple times. I've honed what I want to offer the world and how I'm going to offer it. Sometimes I was forced to change direction because what I offered wasn't what women wanted, and I needed to pay the mortgage. Other times, circumstances or things I found out made me realize my plan needed to pivot. And pivot again. And again. That's all okay, at any stage of life.

It's better to move towards a goal or intention and find it's the wrong one, than to stay stuck in the same position for good. Stay curious. Stay open. That will keep you engaged with the world and able to make what changes you need. Here we go!

STEP 1: DO A MIDLIFE AUDIT

It can be hard not knowing where to start with major changes and improvements to life. There's so much to consider. I'm going to ask you to dream big. As you plan what's next, I want you, first, to take a detailed look at different areas of your life where you may want to make changes, to enable you to play big and do the dream stuff. I know I've asked you to review a lot already, but it's by doing this work in detail that you'll get clarity on what needs to change in the various areas of your life. These areas include where you have issues or would like to focus, what your priorities are for moving forward, and specific next steps you'd like to take. It's useful to establish a baseline from which you can grow. That means getting the basics down, at least relatively well, so we have a good, clean baseline and not a lumpy, fractured one from which to start with the big stuff.

You'll review seven life areas, and now's the time, if you haven't already, to get really honest with yourself about how your life is right now. For each of these areas, I'd like you to write down in your notebook, on a scale of one to ten, how comfortable you are with this area of your life. One is "not at all comfortable," five is "just okay," and ten is "extremely comfortable." I'd like you to consider the specific questions under each heading and then give yourself an overall score. You can access a sheet to plug in your answers at magnificentmidlife.com/bookresources.

This life audit is a very powerful exercise if you take the time to really consider your responses. Any life area for which you score below a seven really needs attention. Anything below a five is a red flag for focus.

Journal in your notebook about any specific thoughts that come up for you.

To guide your response, consider the questions below for each individual section, jotting down ideas in your notebook, and then score yourself overall on the scale.

Section 1: Financial security

Things to consider:

- How well do you know your financial situation?
- Do you have debt?
- Do you have a pension and or savings?
- Do you know if your pension will cover your needs in retirement and or later life?
- Are you saving now for your future?
- Do you have an emergency fund?

- What can you do right now to feel more financially secure?

How comfortable are you with this area of your life on a scale of 1-10? (One is "not at all comfortable," five is "just okay," ten is "extremely comfortable.")

1   2   3   4   5   6   7   8   9   10

Section 2: Career or work

Things to consider:

- Do you live to work or work to live?
- Do you have a feeling you should be doing something else and or more?
- Have you already identified a different dream job?
- Can you work out whether it's financially feasible to follow your dream?
- Could the dream initially be a side hustle?
- Can you think of one action step to improve your work life?

How comfortable are you with this area of your life on a scale of 1-10?

1   2   3   4   5   6   7   8   9   10

Section 3: Caring and other commitments

Things to consider:

- What caring commitments do you have? Children/parents/other?
- Are you able to prioritize yourself and your needs?
- Is an (impending) empty nest causing concern?

- Do you need and or can you access help with your caring commitments?
- If you don't have children, are you wondering what your role is now? Are you coping with the transition into life post menopause and how your peer group may be moving on to a new stage?
- How can you prioritize yourself more if you have a lot of caring commitments?

How comfortable are you with this area of your life on a scale of 1-10?

1   2   3   4   5   6   7   8   9   10

Section 4: Health and well-being

Things to consider:

- Are you generally in good health?
- Can you improve your general health?
- Do you have a good level of fitness?
- Do you prioritize movement and getting enough exercise?
- Do you maintain a good diet that works for the stage of life you are at now?
- Are your hormones sufficiently balanced, or do they cause you problems?
- Are you focusing on all this now, having read Chapters 5-8?

How comfortable are you with this area of your life on a scale of 1-10?

1   2   3   4   5   6   7   8   9   10

Section 5: Relationships

Things to consider:

- How good are your key relationships?
- Does your primary relationship bring you joy?
- Would you like a new primary relationship?
- What can you do to improve and or maintain the quality of your relationships?
- Do your long-term friendships still serve you?
- Would you like to make new friends?
- What's one thing you could easily do to improve your relationships?

How comfortable are you with this area of your life on a scale of 1-10?

1   2   3   4   5   6   7   8   9   10

Section 6: Style

Things to consider:

- Are you comfortable with your clothes, hair, and general sense of style?
- Have they changed over time, or are you stuck in a rut?
- Does your style reflect who you are now or who you want to be?
- Have you succumbed to ageist stereotypes in terms of how you "should" look or dress now?
- What changes might you make to update your look?

How comfortable are you with this area of your life on a scale of 1-10?

1   2   3   4   5   6   7   8   9   10

Section 7: Fulfilment, purpose, and legacy

Things to consider:

- Is there something you've always wanted to do but now fear it's too late?
- What's your wildest dream?
- Do you feel fulfilled and that life has a purpose?
- Have you considered what your obituary might say, and are you happy with that?
- Is there anything you regret not having done?
- Have you written your will?
- How might you bring more of a sense of purpose into your life right now?

How comfortable are you with this area of your life on a scale of 1-10?

1   2   3   4   5   6   7   8   9   10

Well done! You've completed the first stage of the midlife audit.

STEP 2: RECOGNIZE AREAS OF FOCUS

Once you've scored yourself in each area, go back through the sections and consider the following questions for each area. You can fill in your answers on the sheet at magnificentmidlife.com/bookresources.

- What's good about this area of your life?
- What needs improvement in this area of your life?
- Do you need outside help to improve this area? What might that look like?
- Is this an area of focus for you, yes or no? If yes, do you need help, and what might that look like?

How do you feel now? Don't worry if it's rather overwhelming. This plan is about improvement over time; it doesn't have to all be done at once. Hopefully, you now have more clarity on areas to focus on and things you'd benefit from getting sorted, so you can move on to the good stuff. You can always get help to work through this list, with mentoring from me, for example! This is such a simple process, but many of us aren't intentional enough about life to actually go through it. Sometimes we get so caught up in the busyness of our lives that it's difficult to see an alternative way forward. If we break life down and tackle different aspects in their individual component parts, the big, tangled mess can become much more manageable.

If nothing else, you'll now know what areas could do with some focus to improve what's not working and where you can relax. I'd like you to go back to the exercise and think about three action steps you can take in each area that needs focus, and where you want to make changes. Note those action steps down in your notebook or on the sheet. This is the beginning of your plan, improving your life as it is now, so you can lay the groundwork for creating your new one.

- What are your areas of focus?
- What are your first action steps?

STEP 3: REVIEW THE PAST

Next, I'd like you to take a good look at your past. Start by reviewing what you've done over the last decade. Often, we focus on what we haven't achieved rather than what we have. We can forget to take stock of the good things, preferring instead to lament our lack of progress and comparing ourselves negatively with others we presume to be further along the imaginary progress road.

1. What are you proud of? Over the past 10 years, what have you done that you're proud of, what obstacles have you overcome, and what have you achieved? You could pull out old photos or calendars to jog your memory. It could be trips you made, vegetables you grew in your garden—anything that you're pleased to have done. I found photos I'd saved on Facebook to be a fantastic aide-memoire for this. What was important, and why? Write a list and think about what these mean to you, and why.

2. What have you learned? Think about what you've learned over the last 10 years. What wisdom have you accumulated from mistakes made or things that went well? I like to think of anything going wrong as an opportunity to learn something! Write it all down.

3. What are you willing to let go of? We've already covered a lot of this topic in the last chapter, but feel free to add anything here you may have missed. Are there things you feel you "should" do but really don't want to? What did you put on your "chuck it" list? What about resentments, anger, and long-term upset? We've talked about limiting

beliefs. Write them down. What are the most important things to let go of, to enable you to make the very most of your magnificent next chapter?

Wow, you're making progress! You've reviewed your life and recorded what you achieved in the last decade. I hope you are pleasantly surprised at just how much you have achieved. When I did this exercise, I was amazed at how much I'd forgotten, such as when I went on a desert trek in Jordan or completed that half marathon the year I turned 50. Or when my choir won Gospel Choir of the Year in the UK! It's really good to wallow in our achievements from time to time.

STEP 4: LOOK TO THE FUTURE

Now, start looking forward. Take out the notes you made in Chapter Nine on exploring possibilities for your future. Review those and keep them in mind as we go through a process of more self-reflection. This will all help you work out where you want to go next, and how to make that happen.

Capturing your ideas on paper or, next best, online, is crucial if you're to make actual change rather than just thinking about it. That's why you started this book, right? This is where you move from thinking to doing. You'll get much more from this book if you do the work!

The first thing you can do to create your magnificent future is dream about what you'd like your life to look like. Take some time to imagine your ideal day. If all the areas we've talked about were sorted and moving along swimmingly, what would your life look like? If you are still working, how many hours do you want to work? Do you want to work for someone else or for yourself? Have you actually always wanted to start a business? How much of your time and mental energy do you want to devote to work if that still needs to be part of your life?

Find somewhere quiet, close your eyes, and imagine yourself sometime in the future. Just how far in the future depends on how far forward you'd like to imagine. You might be comfortable thinking only a year ahead. Be daring and imagine yourself five years or even a decade from now. Where are you living? What do you look like? What have you achieved? How do you spend your days? What does your home look like? Imagine a picture of your life in the future. Really feel it. Hear the sounds, smell the smells, use all your senses to experience the Future You.

Next, open your eyes and get out your notebook. Write down what you saw in your visioning. What does your ideal life look like?

To get there, what do you want to make more time for? Study, exercise, hobbies, relationships, earning money—write down whatever it might be.

How do you want to organize your time? How much is working, how much is leisure or other activities? How much time in each year would you like to use for travel, for example?

Who are the people in your future life? Colleagues, friends, family? If there are new people, what are they like? Write it all down, and imagine how this life might become reality. Factor in your "chuck it" list. Create a new bucket list.

STEP 5: FACTOR IN YOUR VALUES

Next, take a look at your values. Often, we lose sight of what really motivates us day to day. It's crucial to establish what values keep us going, so when we struggle, we can come back to what really matters. For many years, I worked in a high-powered corporate environment. It was exciting for a long time, but as the years went on, I became uncomfortable with it. I wanted to do something else but couldn't work out why my chosen profession no longer sat right with me. It took me a long time to realize it didn't match my values because I'd never really considered my values. The more I started to think about my values and what they meant to me, the more my career became unsustainable. It just didn't make me happy anymore. When we know our values and have committed to them, it's so much easier to fit those to our strengths and find the sweet spot that's going to lead to both achievement and fulfillment.

You may already have a feel for what your values are likely to be. But it's still important to try to narrow them down and focus in on what really matters to you. If you search "Core Values List" online, you'll find lots of examples. Brené Brown has a great list that you can download from her website, for example.[149] Just search "Brené Brown values online," and you'll find it.

Sit with a list, and circle the ones that appeal most. Feel free to add your own. Then give it some time, and try to reduce the number of values to just three. I know that's really hard to do, so if you get stuck at five, I'll let you off the hook! But doing this will provide real focus about what's truly important to you. You can always bunch several values together, too, if you need to.

STEP 6: CONSIDER HOW YOU WANT TO FEEL

Several years ago, I discovered the work of Danielle LaPorte,[150] focused on building lives based on desires, and, specifically, how we want to feel on a daily basis. We've already touched on feelings quite a lot, but Danielle's work takes this to a whole other level. It can be radical for anyone who's not used to prioritizing their feelings as I wasn't until a few years ago.

When asked what my advice to my younger self would be, it's always "follow your heart." It took me a long time to start doing that, and going through Danielle's *Desire Map* process was an important staging point for me.

Most of us do things that cause us to feel a certain way. The action comes first, and the feeling is the result. Danielle's approach requires us to work out how we want to feel and then do things to deliver those feelings. This is such a simple concept, and yet, for me, it was radical. I'd always lived my life thinking about what I needed to achieve, whether that was a certain level of money or specific career success. When I finally worked out how I wanted to feel, I realized I'd been living my life all wrong! No wonder I'd felt so unfulfilled. Turning it all around finally made absolute sense. That's when my life really started to change.

You've looked at key areas of your life and audited what is and isn't working. You're hopefully starting to prioritize areas you feel are important. You've looked at your values, and that's an important step in working out your core desired feelings too—what is and isn't of value to you. If you're a very practical type, you may never before have connected deeply with your heart, soul, and desires.

Essentially, you look at various areas of your life, such as relationships, learning, wellness, and spirituality, and start by thinking about what you are grateful for in these areas (and, conversely, what you're not happy with, and why). It's a bit like the audit above, but this time, the next stage is to really tap into how you'd like to feel in each of those areas of your life. You can brainstorm lists of feelings and work out which apply for you. Then, like the values, you try to reduce the list of feeling words until you have three or four core desired feelings.

I have my core desired feelings stuck up on my office wall, and it's interesting to me that in the six years since I went through this process, they've not changed. Danielle recommends doing this process regularly to make sure you're fully in touch with your current core desired feelings.

My core desired feelings are:

- Inspire (which stands for both inspiring people and being inspired)
- Vibrant
- Centered
- Authentically brilliant (I cheated here, putting two feeling words together!)

Though I often forget to touch base with these, the whole idea is that we connect with our feelings on a daily basis and then live our lives according to those feelings. So I might say to myself, "I'm not feeling very centered today, what do I need to do to change that?" It's a very powerful way of reconnecting with our heart and soul and allowing those to guide us. As Danielle says, "feelings are magnetic. Each feeling is a beacon that attracts a reality."

This process can be truly liberating, enabling us to connect with what we desire rather than chase things that others desire for us or that society expects of us. It's about digging deep, so we can build our lives going forward based on what we want. I highly recommend going through this process to incorporate a more heart- and soul-driven approach to planning your next chapter. You can access all of Danielle's resources on her website.[151]

Once you've worked out your core desired feelings, use those to guide what you want to do, have, and experience. Danielle's question is always, "What do I need to do to feel the way I want to feel?"

STEP 7: BRING IT ALL TOGETHER

Hopefully, by now you'll be seeing themes appearing from all the thinking you've done. There will be clues as to what to take forward and what to leave behind. Continue writing this all down. Then take a week, perhaps, to let it all percolate and simmer in your heart. Try meditating on everything you've discovered about yourself. In your journaling, ask your genius mind what it wants you to know. Keep asking. Looking within is incredibly powerful. Focus on finding what will bring meaning and fulfillment to your life, back that up with living a healthy life as best you can, and you can't go too far wrong.

Decide what you're going to work on first. Look for what will give you the quickest, biggest impact towards living a life that will fit with your values, include your dreams, and allow you to feel the way you want to feel. Break that down into its component parts. Decide what to focus on and how. If that's a new career, for example, work out where it might be or what it'll look like. Is it working for someone else or a new business to set up, part-time or full-time, with what kind of people? Is it a sideways move or an upwards move? Does it use existing skills or require training? Who can help as a referrer or mentor?

If it's revisiting a hobby you loved when younger, think about what you need to buy—a piano, an easel, whatever it might be. What other resources will you need? How will you get any tuition you need? What sort of timescale will you apply to developing your skill, and how will you measure progress? Decide when and how you'll review your plan and where you'll get advice or help when you encounter roadblocks along the way. Be open to anything and anyone who can help you realize your dreams, goals, or intentions. Put dates in your diary for when you'll check in with your plan and progress. Make those weekly, monthly, or bi-monthly—whatever works for you.

The Japanese have a wonderful concept called *ikigai*. It's the place where your needs, desires, ambitions, and satisfaction meet. It's closely linked to a long and happy life. In the book, *Ikigai: The Japanese Secret to a Long and Happy Life*, Hector Garcia writes:

"Our *ikigai* is different for all of us, but one thing we have in common is that we are all searching for meaning. When we spend our days feeling connected to what is meaningful to us, we live more fully; when we lose the connection, we feel despair... Our intuition and curiosity are very powerful internal compasses to help us connect with our *ikigai*."[152]

Midlife is this wonderful period in our lives to take the time, do the work, find out who we are now, and decide what we want for the rest of our lives. Finding and following our *ikigai* is closely correlated with our future happiness. If we don't already have it by midlife, it's about bloody time we moved closer to finding it. While it's never too late, the clock is ticking. So get out there and take up the challenge! Because we deserve to live happy and fulfilled lives at any stage of life. And the world needs the wisdom and experience of older women now more than ever. We need ourselves to be on top form, and the world needs that too.

In 2009, the Dalai Lama, talking in the context of world peace, said he believes the world will be saved by the Western woman. I think he said "Western" because Western women have so many resources at our disposal. Women anywhere may create a lot of our own limitations in terms of lacking self-belief and confidence, but Western women have fewer actual limitations on their lives than women in so many other parts of the world. I believe the world can be saved by all women stepping forward, but especially us older ones who are growing into our power and grace and authority. Now's our time!

As I said before, we women generally don't create wars. We collaborate and nurture. We build communities, not put up walls to separate them. We reach across the divide naturally way more than men do. We start fewer nasty fights. I believe the world needs more of that. I also believe that the older we get, the more powerful we get. It's time for us to step forward, not step back, in both our own lives and for the good of the world. I hope you'll join me in your magnificent midlife and beyond.

Now it's over to you!

STARTING NOW TO MAKE YOUR PLAN A REALITY

Thank you for following along this far. Knowledge is power! Without it, life (and we) can get very stuck. With it, the world can open up to all sorts of possibilities.

If you're feeling a bit stuck in information overload, just breathe! Take some time for everything to percolate for a while. Maybe take some time off before reading or doing any more. I won't hold it against you. Change can be scary. Believe me, I know.

Let's recap what we've covered.

We've looked at how the world lied to us. Midlife, menopause, and aging are not bad at all. In fact, they can be the impetus for the most exciting time of our life, as long as we recognize all the toxic narratives for what they are—toxic.

We've seen that just because ageist, sexist narratives are there, and we've grown up with them, it doesn't mean they're true. We can look to the example of other cultures and our own role models and pick and choose the narratives that most serve us and enable us to best serve the world as we grow.

You've indulged my efforts to rebrand menopause completely and have been deluged with all the different ways to manage it, so you can flourish through it and feel its truly transformational impact (in a good way). Now that you've completed the process, you may find that next time a friend complains about menopause, you'll know exactly how to help her. (And your daughters, goddaughters, nieces, friendly neighbors and their partners, should they ever need some good down-to-earth advice!)

You've built on your knowledge about managing menopause to enable you to enjoy wellness long term. You know the basics of how to age well, both physically and emotionally, and you know where to get more information on this if you want to dig deeper.

I hope there's now a new lens through which you view midlife and the future, and that you're open to the myriad possibilities ahead of you. You'll have a much better idea of who you are now, your strengths, and what's going to excite you and help you feel fulfilled going forward.

You've also taken a deep dive into what you want to take forward into your next chapter and what you definitely want to leave behind. Perhaps you've even done a little retreat work to mark your transition and have taken a good honest look at your relationships, whether they still serve you, and what you can do to fix any issues there. You've also had a look at any unresolved issues, so you can fix or ditch them, plus any behavior patterns that hold you back.

You've been really honest with yourself about what's working and what isn't.

Next, you did an audit of how your life looks now and what you've achieved in recent years. You've considered your values and how you want to feel. Hopefully, you've thought in depth about what you want to do next with your one precious life.

Wow—you've covered so much! Kudos for taking these important steps toward really embracing your midlife with zeal and imagination.

WELL DONE!

So, what's next? Well, the world is your oyster, my dear. I hope your morale has felt a boost and you're now excited by the knowledge of exactly what you need to do to age well and have the very best chance of a magnificent midlife and beyond. I want you to take control of the next phase of life, to make it everything you ever hoped it could be, so when you look back 10 or 20 or even 30 years from now, you can say, "Yup, I made the most of my one precious life." In whatever way that works for you. Big or small, it's all good.

I've been guilty in the past of buying books, putting them on my shelf and then trying to read them by osmosis. I've actually read other books, then put them aside, and in a couple of weeks, I've forgotten what was in them. If you've really done the exercises in this book, you're further along the memory route than I was for a long time with other great books I've read. If you haven't done the exercises yet, go back and do them! You'll appreciate the effort once you see the immense changes they can make in your life.

Even if you just take one small step each day, that's a start. Imagine after a month, you'll have taken 30+ steps towards change. After six months, it's 180+ steps towards creating the life you want. How would you feel then, knowing you're taking control of your life?

Doing this work is hard, especially trying to do it alone. Doing it without some personal accountability can be really tough. Change usually is. Fear and imposter syndrome will keep popping up as a way to keep you safe. Because if nothing changes, that's safe, right? Well, not exactly. I hope I've shown you why that's not true. If doing what you'd like to do seems tough to do alone, I would love to offer you more support! Check out my 1:1 mentoring or my group programs and online membership to see how those can help. You can find out more at magnificentmidlife.com.

I'm excited for your future. I'm excited about what an army of empowered older women can do to change the world, to disrupt the status quo, and to bring about real positive change for ourselves, our younger friends, daughters, nieces, and the planet. Let's get started.

To your magnificence!

Rachel x

THE 34 SYMPTOMS
OF PERIMENOPAUSE
AND MENOPAUSE

Here's the list of 34 symptoms associated with perimenopause and menopause. The most common ones are marked
with *.

Hot flushes/flashes*

Night sweats*

Irregular periods*

Mood swings*

Vaginal dryness*

Decreased libido*

Headaches

Breast soreness

Burning mouth

Joint pain

Digestive problems

Electric shocks

Muscle tension

Gum problems

Tingling extremities

Itchy skin

Fatigue*

Anxiety*

Disrupted sleep*

Hair loss

Memory lapses*

Difficulty concentrating*

Weight gain*

Dizzy spells

Bloating

Stress incontinence

Brittle nails

Allergies

Irregular heartbeat

Body odor

Irritability*

Depression*

Panic disorder

Osteoporosis

MY SELF-CARE HABITS

It can be overwhelming working out what to incorporate in a long-term health plan. Where do you start? "I don't want more on my to-do list!!" I hear you say! But it needn't be too hard. As well as trying to eat well and reduce toxins in my environment, here's what works for me, by way of example. I realize it's easier for me as I work from home. But even if you have less flexibility because you work outside the home or have caring responsibilities, for example, putting some of these habits in place should be pretty doable.

I run or walk most days, especially during the pandemic. Mostly, I cover 3-5 km , walking a bit, running a bit, changing the ratio of running to walking depending on how I feel. I mostly do this first thing in the morning, as I like to exercise when I'm fresh and get my steps in on my Fitbit for the day. If I'm going bonkers and do an 8 km run or walk, I've done my 10,000 steps before breakfast.

If I'm doing a longer run or walk, I now try to make sure I first have at least something small to eat or drink, like fruit juice, for example. In 2018, I was on holiday in Turkey and fainted after doing a lot of exercise on an empty stomach. I felt great, but my body was clearly suffering, and my blood sugar level dropped dramatically. I ended up with 14 stitches in my face and a scar through my left eyebrow (fortunately hardly noticeable now). You can read all about this on the

Magnificent Midlife blog.[153] It reminded me about the need to maintain a constant blood sugar level!

I also do yoga at least twice a week. I've been an Ashtanga yoga devotee for many years. It took me several years to work up to this, though, having started with a gentle Hatha practice. Nowadays, I try to mix things up a bit, so I'll try to do one Ashtanga class each week and then something else, either a gentle Yin yoga class or another kind of Vinyasa (flow) class. Most days, I try to do at least some sun salutations and leg stretches at home. If I manage that, I feel better all around.

I'm also trying to do a bit of daily weightlifting. I have an assortment of dumbbells, kettle bells, and resistance bands at home. Doing just five minutes a day of arm exercises with an eight-pound dumbbell can help maintain my muscles and metabolism. I'm trying to create a daily habit, rather than doing just 30 minutes two or three times a week, as suggested by Dr. Glenville. But do whatever works!

In terms of my emotional well-being, I rely on meditating, journaling, and nature, in particular. My daily runs or walks connect me with nature and are great for stress relief. I try to meditate whenever I remember. That's not every day, but I would like it to be. I've tried all different types of meditation: mindfulness, Zen, counting and guided meditations. Recently I've been trying my own version of Transcendental Meditation. I've chosen my own mantra and repeat that in my head while sitting for 20 minutes. I'm really enjoying it now that I've stopped stressing about how to get it exactly right (never having done the course), but just doing what best suits me.

I'd like to try more of the Kirtan Kriya meditation I mentioned, but that requires having no one around to listen to
me chanting! I also really enjoy the Calm[154] app, which offers
a daily 10 minute mindfulness meditation. Who doesn't have
10 minutes right?

I long fought against daily journaling, though I've known for
years how powerful it can be. Then I read *The Artist's Way*
and finally embraced it, and now I love it. Again, it's not every
day, but I try to journal often. It's a great way of emptying
my head.

Then, on the weekend, I try to get out in nature for a long
walk. A walk in the woods ticks all the boxes for me!

BIBLIOGRAPHY

Allen, Katherine. *The Qigong Bible*. Godsfield Press, 2017.

Applewhite, Ashton. *This Chair Rocks: A Manifesto against Ageism*. Melville House UK, 2019.

Brennan, Sabina. *Beating Brain Fog: Your 30-Day Plan to Think Faster, Sharper, Better*. Orion Spring, 2021.

Brotto, Lori A. *Better Sex through Mindfulness: How Women Can Cultivate Desire*. Greystone Books, 2018.

Calimeris, Dorothy and Lulu Cook. *The Complete Anti-Inflammatory Diet for Beginners: A No-Stress Meal Plan with Easy Recipes to Heal the Immune System*. Rockridge Press, 2017.

Duffell, Sally J. *Grow Your Own HRT: Sprout Hormone-Rich Greens in Only Two Minutes a Day*. Findhorn Press Ltd., 2017.

Frankl, Viktor E. *Man's Search for Meaning: The Classic Tribute to Hope from the Holocaust*. Rider, 2004.

Gilbert, Elizabeth. *Big Magic: How to Live a Creative Life, and Let Go of Your Fear*. Bloomsbury Paperbacks, 2016.

Glenville, Marilyn. *Fat Around the Middle: How to Lose That Bulge for Good and Why It's Not All Down to Diet*. Kyle Books, 2006.

Gottman, John. *The Seven Principles for Making Marriage Work*. Orion, 2007.

Gottman, John. *The Seven Principles for Making Marriage Work: A Practical Guide from the International Bestselling Relationship Expert*. Orion Spring, 2018.

Gunter, Jen. *The Menopause Manifesto: Own Your Health with Facts and Feminism*. Toronto: Random House Canada, 2021.

Huffington, Arianna. *On Becoming Fearless: A Road Map for Women*. Little, Brown & Company, 2006.

Huffington, Arianna. *The Sleep Revolution: Transforming Your Life, One Night at a Time*. WH Allen, 2017.

LeMay, Ruxandra. *My Spouse Wants More Sex than Me: The 2-Minute Solution for a Happier Marriage*. Amazon, 2015.

Lynch, Jackie. *The Happy Menopause: Smart Nutrition to Help You Flourish*. Watkins Publishing, 2020.

Mathews, Meg. *The New Hot: Taking on the Menopause with Attitude and Style.* Vermilion, 2020.

Mohr, Tara. *Playing Big: A Practical Guide for Brilliant Women like You.* Arrow, 2015.

Moran, Caitlin. *More than a Woman.* Ebury Press, 2020.

Mosconi, Lisa. *The XX Brain: The Groundbreaking Science Empowering Women to Prevent Dementia.* Allen & Unwin, 2020.

Nagoski, Emily. *Come as You Are: The Bestselling Guide to the New Science That Will Transform Your Sex Life: 1.* Scribe UK, 2015.

Perel, Esther. *Mating in Captivity: How to Keep Desire and Passion Alive in Long-Term Relationships.* Hodder & Stoughton, 2007.

Rauch, Jonathan. *The Happiness Curve: Why Life Gets Better after 50.* Thomas Dunne Books, 2018.

Saunders, Susan. *The Age-Well Plan: The 6-Week Programme to Kickstart a Longer, Healthier, Happier Life.* Piatkus Books, 2022.

Steinke, Darcey. *Flash Count Diary: A New Story about the Menopause.* Canongate Books, 2019.

Streets, Annabel and Susan Saunders. *The Age Well Project: Easy Ways to a Longer, Healthier, Happier Life.* London: Piatkus, 2021.

Williamson, Marianne. *By Marianne Williamson – A Return to Love.* Thorsons, 1996.

Zander, Rosamund Stone and Benjamin Zander. *The Art of Possibility: Transforming Professional and Personal Life.* Penguin, 2006.

Zander, Rosamund Stone and Ben Zander. *Pathways to Possibility: Transform Your Outlook on Life with the Bestselling Author of the Art of Possibility.* Penguin, 2017.

ENDNOTES

1   "Follicle-Stimulating Hormone (FSH) Test," Healthline, July 9, 2012, https://www.healthline.com/health/fsh#purpose.
2   "Charity for Women with POI | the Daisy Network," https://www.daisynetwork.org/.
3   Anthony Cuthbertson, "How Female Leaders Outperformed Men During the Pandemic," The Independent, July 24, 2020, https://www.independent.co.uk/news/world/coronavirus-cases-women-men-leaders-countries-data-a9635396.html.
4   "This Chair Rocks," This Chair Rocks, 2016, https://thischairrocks.com/.
5   Ashton Applewhite, Let's End Ageism, Ted.com, https://www.ted.com/talks/ashton_applewhite_let_s_end_ageism?language=en.
6   Ashton Applewhite, This Chair Rocks: A Manifesto against Ageism, Amazon (Networked Books, 2016). https://www.amazon.co.uk/This-Chair-Rocks-Manifesto-Against/dp/0996934707.
7   Bryanne Salazar, "20 Oldest Celebrities to Become Dads," mom.com, September 26, 2017, https://mom.com/entertainment/45577-20-oldest-hollywood-stars-who-became-dads/mick-jagger.
8   "Out of the Bubble Podcast with Rachel Peru," Out of the Bubble, August 20, 2021, https://www.rachelperu.co.uk/.
9   "Episode 9: First Time Modelling in Your 40s with Rachel Peru," Magnificent Midlife, April 16, 2019, https://magnificentmidlife.com/podcast/episode-9-first-time-modelling-in-your-40s-with-rachel-peru/.
10 Market Data Forecast Ltd, "Anti-Aging Market Size, Share, Trends, Growth Analysis Report | 2020 to 2025," Market Data Forecast, February 2020, https://www.marketdataforecast.com/market-reports/anti-aging-market.
11 "Tao Porchon-Lynch," Wikipedia, June 14, 2020, https://en.wikipedia.org/wiki/Tao_Porchon-Lynch.

12 "America's Got Talent 2015 S10E03 Tao Porchon Lynch and Vard 96 Year Old Dancer," www.youtube.com, June 11, 2015, https://www.youtube.com/watch?v=xauVlSaaraA.

13 Giuseppe Passarino, Francesco De Rango, and Alberto Montesanto, "Human Longevity: Genetics or Lifestyle? It Takes Two to Tango," Immunity & Ageing 13, no. 1 (April 5, 2016), doi.org/10.1186/s12979-016-0066-z.

14 Becca Levy et al., "(PDF) Subliminal Strengthening: Improving Older Individuals' Physical Function over Time with an Implicit-Age-Stereotype Intervention," ResearchGate, October 2014, https://www.researchgate. net/publication/267043642_Subliminal_Strengthening_ Improving_Older_Individuals%27_Physical_Function_Over_ Time_With_an_Implicit-Age-Stereotype_Intervention.

15 David Robson, "The Age You Feel Means More than Your Actual Birthdate," bbc.com (BBC Future, 2018), https://www. bbc.com/future/article/20180712-the-age-you-feel-means-more-than-your-actual-birthdate.

16 "Silver Economy Study: How to Stimulate the Economy by Hundreds of Millions of Euros per Year | Shaping Europe's Digital Future," digital-strategy.ec.europa.eu, May 3, 2018, https://digital-strategy.ec.europa.eu/en/library/silver-economy-study-how-stimulate-economy-hundreds-millions-euros-year.

17 Kavan Peterson, "The Manifesto against Ageism Is Here," ChangingAging, March 15, 2016, https://changingaging.org/ blog/the-manifesto-against-ageism-is-here/.

18 Ashton Applewhite, This Chair Rocks: A Manifesto against Ageism, Amazon (Melville House UK, 2019), 12. https:// www.amazon.co.uk/This-Chair-Rocks-Ashton-Applewhite/ dp/1911545264/.

19 Jonathan Rauch, The Happiness Curve: Why Life Gets Better after 50, Amazon (Thomas Dunne Books, 2018). https://www. amazon.co.uk/Happiness-Curve-Better-After-International/ dp/1250078806/.

20 Guardian Staff, "Are You Really at Your Most Miserable at 47.2 Years Old?," the Guardian, January 14, 2020, https://www. theguardian.com/lifeandstyle/shortcuts/2020/jan/14/are-you-really-at-your-most-miserable-at-47-years-old.

21 "The Death Clock - When Am I Going to Die?," www. deathclock.com, http://www.deathclock.com/.

22 Arianna Stassinopoulos Huffington, On Becoming Fearless: A Road Map for Women, Amazon (Little, Brown & Company, 2006), https://www.amazon.co.uk/Becoming-Fearless-Road-Map-Women/dp/0316166820/.

23 Karina Martinez-Carter, "How the Elderly Are Treated around the World," Theweek.com (The Week, July 23, 2013), https://theweek.com/articles/462230/how-elderly-are-treated-around-world.

24 Karina Martinez-Carter, "How the Elderly Are Treated around the World," Theweek.com (The Week, July 23, 2013), https://theweek.com/articles/462230/how-elderly-are-treated-around-world.

25 "7 Cultures That Celebrate Aging and Respect Their Elders," HuffPost (HuffPost, February 25, 2014), https://www.huffpost.com/entry/what-other-cultures-can-teach_n_4834228.

26 Corinna E. Löckenhoff et al., "Perceptions of Aging across 26 Cultures and Their Culture-Level Associates.," Psychology and Aging 24, no. 4 (2009): 941–54, https://doi.org/10.1037/a0016901.

27 Achyut Bihani and Faye Wang, "In Your Country, What Is the Role of Elderly People?," Slate Magazine, May 30, 2013, https://slate.com/human-interest/2013/05/in-your-country-what-is-the-role-of-elderly-people.html.

28 "Honorific," Wikipedia, August 15, 2021, https://en.wikipedia.org/wiki/Honorific.

29 "Hā Kūpuna," Hā Kūpuna, http://manoa.hawaii.edu/hakupuna/.

30 Kate Devlin, "British Women 'Suffer Symptoms of Menopause More than Those in Other Countries,'" www.telegraph.co.uk, June 8, 2010, https://www.telegraph.co.uk/news/health/news/7808596/British-women-suffer-symptoms-of-menopause-more-than-those-in-other-countries.html.

31 Emma K Jones et al., "Menopause and the Influence of Culture: Another Gap for Indigenous Australian Women?," BMC Women's Health 12, no. 1 (December 2012), https://doi.org/10.1186/1472-6874-12-43.

32 Emma K Jones et al., "Menopause and the Influence of Culture: Another Gap for Indigenous Australian Women?," BMC Women's Health 12, no. 1 (December 2012), https://doi.org/10.1186/1472-6874-12-43.

33   Darcey Steinke, Flash Count Diary: A New Story about the Menopause, Amazon (Canongate Books, 2019), https://www.amazon.co.uk/Flash-Count-Diary-Story-Menopause/dp/178689811X/ref=sr_1_1?dchild=1&keywords=flash+count+diary&qid=1601198996&sr=8-1.

34   "Episode 20: The Magic of Menopause with Darcey Steinke," Magnificent Midlife, August 14, 2019, https://magnificentmidlife.com/podcast/episode-20-the-magic-of-menopause-with-darcey-steinke/.

35   Tania Elfersy, "Debunking the Biggest Myth of Perimenopause & Menopause," The Wiser Woman, November 21, 2018, https://www.thewiserwoman.com/post/2018/11/21/the-estrogen-theory-ends-here-debunking-the-biggest-myth-surrounding-perimenopause-and-me.

36   Jen Gunter, The Menopause Manifesto : Own Your Health with Facts and Feminism (Toronto: Random House Canada, 2021), 13-14, https://www.amazon.com/Menopause-Manifesto-Health-Facts-Feminism/dp/0806540664/.

37   JP Griffin, "Changing Life Expectancy throughout History," Journal of the Royal Society of Medicine 101, no. 12 (December 2008): 577–77, https://doi.org/10.1258/jrsm.2008.08k037.

38   "Episode 44: Supporting Our Hormonal Balance and Immune System with Angela Counsel," Magnificent Midlife, June 29, 2020, https://magnificentmidlife.com/podcast/44-menopause-hormones-immune-systems-angela-counsel/.

39   Tania Elfersy, "Debunking the Biggest Myth of Perimenopause & Menopause," The Wiser Woman, November 21, 2018, https://www.thewiserwoman.com/post/2018/11/21/the-estrogen-theory-ends-here-debunking-the-biggest-myth-surrounding-perimenopause-and-me.

40   Meg Mathews, The New Hot: Taking on the Menopause with Attitude and Style, Amazon (Vermilion, 2020), https://www.amazon.co.uk/New-Hot-Taking-Menopause-Attitude/dp/178504253X/.

41   Jen Gunter, The Menopause Manifesto : Own Your Health with Facts and Feminism (Toronto: Random House Canada, 2021), 213, https://www.amazon.com/Menopause-Manifesto-Health-Facts-Feminism/dp/0806540664/.

42 Dr. Lisa Mosconi, The XX Brain: The Groundbreaking Science Empowering Women to Prevent Dementia, Amazon (Allen & Unwin, 2020), 179.

43 Dr Lisa Mosconi, The XX Brain: The Groundbreaking Science Empowering Women to Prevent Dementia, Amazon (Allen & Unwin, 2020), 185, https://www.amazon.co.uk/XX-Brain-Groundbreaking-Empowering-Dementia/dp/1911630318/.

44 Wikipedia Contributors, "Blue Zone," Wikipedia (Wikimedia Foundation, July 4, 2019), https://en.wikipedia.org/wiki/Blue_Zone.

45 Jen Gunter, The Menopause Manifesto : Own Your Health with Facts and Feminism (Toronto: Random House Canada, 2021), 227, https://www.amazon.com/Menopause-Manifesto-Health-Facts-Feminism/dp/0806540664/.

46 Meg Mathews, The New Hot: Taking on the Menopause with Attitude and Style, Amazon (Vermilion, 2020), 235, https://www.amazon.co.uk/New-Hot-Taking-Menopause-Attitude/dp/178504253X/.

47 Jackie Lynch, The Happy Menopause: Smart Nutrition to Help You Flourish, Amazon (Watkins Publishing, 2020), https://www.amazon.co.uk/Happy-Menopause-Nutritional-Choices-Flourish/dp/178678372X/.

48 Jo Adetunji, "The Brain Also Produces the Sex Hormone Oestrogen," The Conversation, December 14, 2013, https://theconversation.com/the-brain-also-produces-the-sex-hormone-oestrogen-21194.

49 "Carbohydrates and Blood Sugar," The Nutrition Source, July 25, 2016, https://www.hsph.harvard.edu/nutritionsource/carbohydrates/carbohydrates-and-blood-sugar/.

50 "Study Shows Diet Causes 84% Drop in Troublesome Menopausal Symptoms—without Drugs," Physicians Committee for Responsible Medicine, July 14, 2021, https://www.pcrm.org/news/news-releases/study-shows-diet-causes-84-drop-troublesome-menopausal-symptoms-without-drugs.

51 Chan Ho Jang et al., "Fermented Soy Products: Beneficial Potential in Neurodegenerative Diseases," Foods 10, no. 3 (March 18, 2021), https://doi.org/10.3390/foods10030636.

52 Sally J. Duffell, Grow Your Own HRT: Sprout Hormone-Rich Greens in Only Two Minutes a Day, Amazon (Findhorn Press Ltd., 2017). https://www.amazon.co.uk/Grow-Your-Own-HRT-hormone-rich/dp/1844097374/.

53 "PAN UK Home," Pesticide Action Network UK, n.d., https://www.pan-uk.org/.

54 "EWG," EWG, 2019, https://www.ewg.org/.

55 Tasha Stoiber, "What Are Parabens, and Why Don't They Belong in Cosmetics? | Environmental Working Group," www.ewg.org, April 9, 2019, https://www.ewg.org/what-are-parabens.

56 "Women Put an Average of 168 Chemicals on Their Bodies Each Day, Consumer Group Says," ABC News, April 28, 2015, https://abcnews.go.com/Health/women-put-average-168-chemicals-bodies-day-consumer/story?id=30615324.

57 Dr. Lisa Mosconi, The XX Brain: The Groundbreaking Science Empowering Women to Prevent Dementia, Amazon (Allen & Unwin, 2020), 288, https://www.amazon.co.uk/XX-Brain-Groundbreaking-Empowering-Dementia/dp/1911630318/.

58 Kristen Fischer, "Losing Weight May Ease Hot Flashes, Study Finds," WebMD, July 10, 2014, https://www.webmd.com/menopause/news/20140710/losing-weight-may-ease-hot-flashes-study-finds.

59 "Menopause Makeover," Harvard Health, July 16, 2015, https://www.health.harvard.edu/womens-health/menopause-makeover.

60 Jade Heejae Ko and Seung-Nam Kim, "A Literature Review of Women's Sex Hormone Changes by Acupuncture Treatment: Analysis of Human and Animal Studies," Evidence-Based Complementary and Alternative Medicine 2018 (November 15, 2018): 1–9, https://doi.org/10.1155/2018/3752723.

61 "The Flock Facebook Group," www.facebook.com, https://www.facebook.com/groups/magnificentmidlifeflock/posts/1108883792626547.

62 Sam Norton, Joseph Chilcot, and Myra S. Hunter, "Cognitive-Behavior Therapy for Menopausal Symptoms (Hot Flushes and Night Sweats)," Menopause 21, no. 6 (June 2014): 574–78, https://doi.org/10.1097/gme.0000000000000095.

63 Suzi Grant, "Eat Your Way out of the Menopause - before during & After," Alternative Ageing, https://www.alternativeageing.net/blog/2016/8/29/eat-your-way-out-of-the-menopause-before-during-after.

64 "Suicides in England and Wales - Office for National Statistics," www.ons.gov.uk, September 1, 2020, https://www.ons.gov.uk/peoplepopulationandcommunity/birthsdeathsandmarriages/deaths/bulletins/suicidesintheunitedkingdom/2019registrations#suicide-patterns-by-age.

65 Noma Nazish, "How to De-Stress in 5 Minutes or Less, according to a Navy SEAL," Forbes, May 30, 2019, https://www.forbes.com/sites/nomanazish/2019/05/30/how-to-de-stress-in-5-minutes-or-less-according-to-a-navy-seal/.

66 "Emotional Freedom Therapy for PTSD – PTSD UK," PTSDUK, https://www.ptsduk.org/emotional-freedom-therapy/.

67 "The Tapping Solution (EFT): How to Get Started," www.thetappingsolution.com, n.d., https://www.thetappingsolution.com/.

68 "Loving Essential Oils | DIY Essential Oil Recipes, Diffuser Blends, Aromatherapy Supplies," www.lovingessentialoils.com, n.d., https://www.lovingessentialoils.com/.

69 Jen Gunter, The Menopause Manifesto : Own Your Health with Facts and Feminism (Toronto: Random House Canada, 2021), 114, https://www.amazon.com/Menopause-Manifesto-Health-Facts-Feminism/dp/0806540664/.

70 Arianna Huffington, The Sleep Revolution: Transforming Your Life, One Night at a Time, Amazon (WH Allen, 2017), https://www.amazon.co.uk/Sleep-Revolution-Transforming-Your-Night/dp/0753557215/.

71 "The Tapping Solution (EFT): How to Get Started," www.thetappingsolution.com, n.d., https://www.thetappingsolution.com/.

72 Dr. Sabina Brennan, Beating Brain Fog: Your 30-Day Plan to Think Faster, Sharper, Better, Amazon (Orion Spring, 2021), https://www.amazon.co.uk/Beating-Brain-Fog-30-Day-Sharper-ebook/dp/B08C7PHJRH.

73 Ana Gotter, "The Link between Magnesium and Restless Leg Syndrome," Healthline (Healthline Media, March 2, 2017), https://www.healthline.com/health/restless-leg-syndrome/link-between-magnesium-and-rls.

74 Dorothy Calimeris and Lulu Cook, The Complete Anti-Inflammatory Diet for Beginners: A No-Stress Meal Plan with Easy Recipes to Heal the Immune System, Amazon (Rockridge Press, 2017), https://www.amazon.co.uk/Complete-Anti-Inflammatory-Diet-Beginners-No-Stress/dp/1623159040/.

75 "The Truth about Nightshades and Arthritis," Living With Arthritis, February 21, 2017, http://blog.arthritis.org/living-with-arthritis/nightshades-arthritis/.

76 Marilyn Glenville, Fat around the Middle: How to Lose That Bulge for Good and Why It's Not All down to Diet, Amazon (Kyle Books, 2006), 8, https://www.amazon.co.uk/Fat-Around-Middle-Lose-Bulge/dp/1856266559.

77 NHS, "Healthy Weight," NHS, 2018, https://www.nhs.uk/live-well/healthy-weight/bmi-calculator/.

78 "Your Body Fat Percentage: What Does It Mean? | Winchester Hospital," Winchesterhospital.org, 2015, https://www.winchesterhospital.org/health-library/article?id=41373.

79 Marilyn Glenville, Fat around the Middle: How to Lose That Bulge for Good and Why It's Not All down to Diet, Amazon (Kyle Books, 2006), 27, https://www.amazon.co.uk/Fat-Around-Middle-Lose-Bulge/dp/1856266559.

80 Lisa Rapaport, "Metabolism May Not Decline with Age as Previously Thought | Everyday Health," EverydayHealth.com, August 16, 2021, https://www.everydayhealth.com/diet-nutrition/metabolism-may-not-decline-with-age-as-previously-thought/.

81 Shannon Perry, "Intermittent Fasting and Menopause," gennev, July 13, 2017, https://gennev.com/education/intermittent-fasting-menopause.

82 Marilyn Glenville, Fat around the Middle: How to Lose That Bulge for Good and Why It's Not All down to Diet, Amazon (Kyle Books, 2006), https://www.amazon.co.uk/Fat-Around-Middle-Lose-Bulge/dp/1856266559.

83 Esther Perel, Mating in Captivity: How to Keep Desire and Passion Alive in Long-Term Relationships, Amazon (Hodder & Stoughton, 2007), https://www.amazon.co.uk/Mating-Captivity-passion-long-term-relationships/dp/0340943750/.

84 John Gottman, The Seven Principles for Making Marriage Work, Amazon (Orion, 2007), https://www.amazon.co.uk/Seven-Principles-Making-Marriage-Work/dp/0752837265.

85   "Changes in the Vagina and Vulva, Sexual Side Effects of Menopause | the North American Menopause Society, NAMS," www.menopause.org, accessed October 17, 2020, https://www.menopause.org/for-women/sexual-health-menopause-online/changes-at-midlife/changes-in-the-vagina-and-vulva.

86   "How to Play the 3-Minute Game – Betty Martin," Betty Martin, n.d., http://bettymartin.org/how-to-play-the-3-minute-game/.

87   Petra Larmo et al., "Effects of Sea Buckthorn Oil Intake on Vaginal Atrophy in Postmenopausal Women: A Randomized, Double-Blind, Placebo-Controlled Study," Maturitas 79, no. 3 (November 1, 2014): 316–21, https://doi.org/10.1016/j.maturitas.2014.07.010.

88   Ruxandra LeMay, My Spouse Wants More Sex than Me: The 2-Minute Solution for a Happier Marriage, Amazon, 2015, https://www.amazon.co.uk/gp/product/B00W5TXGGY/.

89   Lori A. Brotto, Better Sex through Mindfulness: How Women Can Cultivate Desire, Amazon (Greystone Books, 2018), https://www.amazon.com/Better-Sex-Through-Mindfulness-Cultivate/dp/1771642351/.

90   "Excellence in Continence Care" NHS England (July 2018), https://www.england.nhs.uk/wp-content/uploads/2018/07/excellence-in-continence-care.pdf.

91   "Episode 12: Giggling about Incontinence with Elaine Miller, Gusset Grippers," Magnificent Midlife, June 18, 2019, https://magnificentmidlife.com/podcast/episode-12-giggling-about-incontinence-with-elaine-miller-gusset-grippers/.

92   Marilyn Glenville, Fat around the Middle: How to Lose That Bulge for Good and Why It's Not All down to Diet, Amazon (Kyle Books, 2006), https://www.amazon.co.uk/Fat-Around-Middle-Lose-Bulge/dp/1856266559.

93   Katherine Allen, The Qigong Bible, Amazon (Godsfield Press, 2017), https://www.amazon.co.uk/Qigong-Bible-Godsfield-Bibles/dp/1841814628/.

94   Wikipedia Contributors, "Qigong," Wikipedia (Wikimedia Foundation, May 17, 2019), https://en.wikipedia.org/wiki/Qigong.

95   Wikipedia Contributors, "Tai Chi," Wikipedia (Wikimedia Foundation, November 12, 2019), https://en.wikipedia.org/wiki/Tai_chi.

96   "Sock Doc," Sock-Doc, https://sock-doc.com/.

97 "Barefoot Shoes | Minimalist Footwear | Vivobarefoot UK," Vivobarefoot.com, 2021, https://www.vivobarefoot.com/uk/.

98 Roma Lightsey, "Piriformis Syndrome: Symptoms, Causes, Treatments, Exercises, and More," WebMD, November 13, 2019, https://www.webmd.com/pain-management/guide/piriformis-syndrome-causes-symptoms-treatments.

99 Tom Morrison, "Tom Morrison - YouTube," www.youtube.com, https://www.youtube.com/channel/UC1bHlccT8JOMAWm5wMuzG9A.

100 Caitlin Moran, More than a Woman, Amazon (Ebury Press, 2020), 211, https://www.amazon.co.uk/More-Than-Woman-Caitlin-Moran/dp/1529102758/.

101 "Yoga with Adriene," YouTube, n.d., https://www.youtube.com/user/yogawithadriene.

102 Nicola Napoli et al., "Effects of Dietary Calcium Compared with Calcium Supplements on Estrogen Metabolism and Bone Mineral Density," The American Journal of Clinical Nutrition 85, no. 5 (May 1, 2007): 1428–33, https://doi.org/10.1093/ajcn/85.5.1428.

103 Annabel Streets and Susan Saunders, The Age Well Project : Easy Ways to a Longer, Healthier, Happier Life (London: Piatkus, 2021) Loc 1180.

104 Roman Thaler et al., "Anabolic and Antiresorptive Modulation of Bone Homeostasis by the Epigenetic Modulator Sulforaphane, a Naturally Occurring Isothiocyanate," Journal of Biological Chemistry 291, no. 13 (January 12, 2016): 6754–71, https://doi.org/10.1074/jbc.m115.678235.

105 Annabel Streets and Susan Saunders, The Age Well Project: Easy Ways to a Longer, Healthier, Happier Life (London: Piatkus, 2021) Loc 1200.

106 Jen Gunter, The Menopause Manifesto : Own Your Health with Facts and Feminism (Toronto: Random House Canada, 2021), Chapter 11.

107 FRAX Fracture Risk Assessment Tool, https://www.sheffield.ac.uk/FRAX/tool.aspx.

108 Matthew Walker, Why We Sleep: The New Science of Sleep and Dreams, Amazon (Penguin, 2018), 165, https://www.amazon.co.uk/Why-We-Sleep-Science-Dr.eams/dp/0141983760/.

109 "The Tapping Solution (EFT): How to Get Started," www.thetappingsolution.com, n.d., https://www. thetappingsolution.com/.

110 "Calm," app.www.calm.com, https://app.www.calm.com/.

111 Insight Network, Inc, Insighttimer.com, 2020, https:// insighttimer.com/.

112 Dr. Lisa Mosconi, The XX Brain: The Groundbreaking Science Empowering Women to Prevent Dementia, Amazon (Allen & Unwin, 2020), 288, https://www.amazon.co.uk/XX-Brain-Groundbreaking-Empowering-Dementia/dp/1911630318/.

113 Dr. Lisa Mosconi, The XX Brain: The Groundbreaking Science Empowering Women to Prevent Dementia, Amazon (Allen & Unwin, 2020), 297, https://www.amazon.co.uk/XX-Brain-Groundbreaking-Empowering-Dementia/dp/1911630318/.

114 "Kirtan Kriya Meditation," www.youtube.com, n.d., https:// www.youtube.com/watch?v=jfKEAiwrgeY.

115 Annabel Streets and Susan Saunders, The Age Well Project: Easy Ways to a Longer, Healthier, Happier Life (London: Piatkus, 2021).

116 Susan Saunders, The Age-Well Plan: The 6-Week Programme to Kickstart a Longer, Healthier, Happier Life, Amazon (Piatkus Books, 2022), https://www.amazon.co.uk/Age-Well-Plan-Programme-Kickstart-Healthier/dp/034942554X/.

117 Dr. Lisa Mosconi, The XX Brain: The Groundbreaking Science Empowering Women to Prevent Dementia, Amazon (Allen & Unwin, 2020), 308, https://www.amazon.co.uk/XX-Brain-Groundbreaking-Empowering-Dementia/dp/1911630318/.

118 "Ditching Imposter Syndrome with Clare Josa," Magnificent Midlife, November 17, 2020, https://magnificentmidlife.com/podcast/58-ditching-imposter-syndrome-with-clare-josa/.

119 Barbara Waxman, "The Middlescence Manifesto © Barbara Waxman MS, MPA, PCC" (, 2016), https://barbarawaxman.com/wp-content/uploads/2016/11/Middlescence-Manifesto-Final.pdf.

120 "Get up and Go: Is 54 Really the Age We Lose Our Passion for Life?," the Guardian, October 28, 2020, https://www.theguardian.com/science/2020/oct/28/get-up-and-go-is-54-really-the-age-we-lose-our-passion-for-life.

121 Viktor E. Frankl, Man's Search for Meaning: The Classic Tribute to Hope from the Holocaust, Amazon (Rider, 2004), https://www.amazon.co.uk/Mans-Search-Meaning-classic-Holocaust/dp/1844132390/.

122 Rosamund Stone Zander and Benjamin Zander, The Art of Possibility: Transforming Professional and Personal Life, Amazon (Penguin, 2006), https://www.amazon.co.uk/Art-Possibility-Practices-Leadership-Relationship/dp/0142001104/.

123 Rosamund Stone Zander and Ben Zander, Pathways to Possibility: Transform Your Outlook on Life with the Bestselling Author of the Art of Possibility, Amazon (Penguin, 2017), https://www.amazon.co.uk/Pathways-Possibility-Rosamund-Stone-Zander/dp/1405931841/.

124 Rosamund Stone Zander and Ben Zander, Pathways to Possibility: Transform Your Outlook on Life with the Bestselling Author of the Art of Possibility, Amazon (Penguin, 2017), https://www.amazon.co.uk/Pathways-Possibility-Rosamund-Stone-Zander/dp/1405931841/.

125 Marianne Williamson, By Marianne Williamson - Return to Love, Amazon (Thorsons, 1996), 190-191, https://www.amazon.com/Marianne-Williamson-Return-Love-10/dp/B00HTJUXO8/.

126 Elizabeth Gilbert, Big Magic: How to Live a Creative Life, and Let Go of Your Fear, Amazon (Bloomsbury Paperbacks, 2016), 24, https://www.amazon.co.uk/Big-Magic-Creative-Living-Beyond/dp/1408866757.

127 Gallup Inc, "Compare CliftonStrengths Assessment Options," Gallup.com, https://www.gallup.com/cliftonstrengths/en/253868/popular-cliftonstrengths-assessment-products.aspx..

128 "Free Strengths Test | Find Your Unique Talents and Character Traits," HIGH 5 TEST, 2016, https://high5test.com/.

129 NERIS Analytics Limited, "Free Personality Test | 16Personalities," 16Personalities (NERIS Analytics Limited, 2019), https://www.16personalities.com/free-personality-test.

130 "From Barrister to Performance Coach - Hattie Voelcker," The Mutton Club, August 1, 2019, https://themuttonclub.com/barrister-performance-coach-hattie-voelcker/.

131 "Daniel Pink | NYT and WSJ Bestselling Author of Drive," Daniel H. Pink, 2018, https://www.danpink.com/.

132 Barbara Waxman, "The Middlescence Manifesto © Barbara Waxman MS, MPA, PCC" (2016), https://barbarawaxman.com/wp-content/uploads/2016/11/Middlescence-Manifesto-Final.pdf.

133 Jill Suttie, "How to Find Your Purpose in Midlife," Greater Good, March 8, 2018, https://greatergood.berkeley.edu/article/item/how_to_find_your_purpose_in_midlife?fbclid=IwAR2ciXCBdEMASVJxrnr0nVt1aOk3BjTF2w92 2OBaC5y0tlMF5NC3hBloME8.

134 "Episode 30: Just Doing It and Living the Dream with Jo Moseley," Magnificent Midlife, January 20, 2020, https://magnificentmidlife.com/podcast/episode-30-just-doing-it-and-living-the-dream-with-jo-moseley/.

135 "Hilary Lewin," Hilary Lewin, https://hilarylewin.com/.

136 Gemma Went, "The Secret Habits of Successful Entrepreneurs," UK Business Mentor + Mindset Coach for Online Entrepreneurs, September 3, 2018, https://gemmawent.co.uk/blog/successful-entrepreneurs-habits.

137 Nancy Olson, "Three Ways That Handwriting with a Pen Positively Affects Your Brain," Forbes, May 15, 2016, https://www.forbes.com/sites/nancyolson/2016/05/15/three-ways-that-writing-with-a-pen-positively-affects-your-brain/?sh=d685ade57055.

138 Ellen Bachmeyer, "4 Reasons Why More Women over 50 Are Getting Divorced," Sixty and Me, August 11, 2018, https://sixtyandme.com/4-reasons-why-more-women-over-50-are-getting-divorced/.

139 Rosamund Stone Zander and Benjamin Zander, The Art of Possibility: Transforming Professional and Personal Life, Amazon (Penguin Books, 2002), https://www.amazon.co.uk/dp/B00N1KJ76E/.

140 John Gottman, The Seven Principles for Making Marriage Work: A Practical Guide from the International Bestselling Relationship Expert, Amazon (Orion Spring, 2018), https://www.amazon.co.uk/Seven-Principles-Making-Marriage-Work-ebook/dp/B075WVH7L3/.

141 Dr. Emily Nagoski, Come as You Are: The Bestselling Guide to the New Science That Will Transform Your Sex Life: 1, Amazon (Scribe UK, 2015), https://www.amazon.co.uk/Come-You-Are-surprising-transform/dp/1925228010/.

142 Dr. Emily Nagoski, Come as You Are: The Bestselling Guide to the New Science That Will Transform Your Sex Life: 1, Amazon (Scribe UK, 2015), Loc 1223, https://www.amazon.co.uk/Come-You-Are-surprising-transform/dp/1925228010/.

143 Ruxandra LeMay, My Spouse Wants More Sex than Me: The 2-Minute Solution for a Happier Marriage, Amazon, 2015, https://www.amazon.co.uk/gp/product/B00W5TXGGY/.

144 Rosamund Stone Zander and Ben Zander, Pathways to Possibility: Transform Your Outlook on Life with the Bestselling Author of the Art of Possibility, Amazon (Penguin, 2017), 16, https://www.amazon.co.uk/Pathways-Possibility-Rosamund-Stone-Zander/dp/1405931841/.

145 Rosamund Stone Zander and Ben Zander, Pathways to Possibility: Transform Your Outlook on Life with the Bestselling Author of the Art of Possibility, Amazon (Penguin, 2017), 56, https://www.amazon.co.uk/Pathways-Possibility-Rosamund-Stone-Zander/dp/1405931841/.

146 Molly Beauchemin, "Understanding Ho'oponopono: A Beautiful Hawaiian Prayer for Forgiveness," Grace & Lightness Magazine, June 26, 2020, https://graceandlightness.com/hooponopono-hawaiian-prayer-for-forgiveness/.

147 "Meditation on Lovingkindness," Jack Kornfield, November 2, 2016, https://jackkornfield.com/meditation-on-lovingkindness/.

148 Tara Mohr, Playing Big: A Practical Guide for Brilliant Women like You, Amazon (Arrow, 2015), https://www.amazon.co.uk/Playing-Big-practical-guide-brilliant/dp/0099591529/.

149 Brené Brown, "Dare to Lead," Dare To Lead List of Values, 2018, https://daretolead.brenebrown.com/wp-content/uploads/2019/02/Values.pdf .

150 "Danielle LaPorte," Danielle LaPorte, n.d., https://www.daniellelaporte.com/.

151 "Danielle LaPorte," Danielle LaPorte, n.d., https://www.daniellelaporte.com/.

152 Héctor García and Francesc Miralles, Ikigai: The Japanese Secret to a Long and Happy Life, Amazon (Hutchinson, 2017), Loc 1652, https://www.amazon.co.uk/Ikigai-Japanese-secret-long-happy/dp/178633089X/.

153 Rachel Lankester, "What I Learnt the Hard Way about Facial Scar Treatment!," Magnificent Midlife, January 18, 2020, https://magnificentmidlife.com/blog/facial-scar-treatment/.

154 "Calm," app.www.calm.com, https://app.www.calm.com/.

Printed in Great Britain
by Amazon

69215305R00139